Essential Mathematics

Book 9S

Michael White

Peter Gibson

Elmwood Press

First published 2010 by
Elmwood Press
80 Attimore Road
Welwyn Garden City
Herts. AL8 6LP
Tel. 01707 333232

British Library Cataloguing in Publication Data

© Elmwood Press
The moral rights of the author have been asserted.
Database right Elmwood Press (maker)

ISBN 9781 902 214 818

Numerical answers are published in a separate book (ISBN 9781 902 214 900)

Typeset and illustrated by Domex e-Data Pvt. Ltd., Chennai, India
Printed and bound by NPE Print Communications

CONTENTS

PREFACE

Essential Mathematics Book 9S has been written for pupils in Year 9 who are working within the National Curriculum Level 3–5 Tier. There is a comprehensive NNS guide at the start of the book with references to all topics.

There is no set path through the books but topics appear in the order suggested in the NNS planning charts. Broadly speaking, the book is split into 6 units. There is a Review Section at the end of the first 2 units. There is also plenty of revision material in unit 5 of the book to consolidate Key Stage 3 work. The 20 individual revision tasks could be tackled as a complete block or spread out throughout the year, possibly forming revision homeworks.

The authors recognise that there is a wealth of ideas available for 'starter' activities and many developing opportunities to explore mathematics through the use of ICT. The purpose of this book is to provide the main material for pupils to work at in a systematic way which helps to build up their confidence.

No textbook will have the 'right' amount of material for every class and the authors believe that it is better to have too much material rather than too little.

Each topic is broken down into two sections. Section M is the main activity and should be suitable for all children at this level. Section E is the extension work. Pupils may move naturally onto this work after Section M, or teachers will judge that a number of students should only tackle Section E.

Explanations are kept to a minimum because it is assumed that teachers will explore each topic fully in line with the NNS guidance.

The authors are indebted to the contributions from David Rayner.

Michael White
Peter Gibson

Year 7 material

Numbers and the number system

Integers, powers and roots

132–134 • Understand negative numbers as positions on a number line; order, add and subract positive and negative integers in context.

Algebra

Sequences, functions and graphs

14–18 • Recognise straight-line graphs parallel to the *x*-axis or *y*-axis.

Shape, space and measures

Geometrical reasoning: lines, angles and shapes

51–54 • Identify parallel and perpendicular lines: know the sum of angles at a point, on a straight line and in a triangle, and recognise vertically opposite angles.

Coordinates

62
98–101
138–140
• Use conventions and notation for 2-D coordinates in all four quadrants; find coordinates of points determined by geometric information.

Construction

66, 67 • construct a triangle given two sides and the included angle (SAS) or two angles and the included side (ASA).

Year 8 material

Using and applying mathematics and solve problems

Applying mathematics and solving problems

210–212,
231
• Identify the necessary information to solve a problem; represent problems and interpret solutions in algebraic, geometric or graphical form, using correct notation and appropriate diagrams.

129–131
209
210–212
• Solve more complex problems by breaking them into smaller steps or tasks, choosing and using efficient techniques for calculation.

Numbers and the number system

Place value, ordering and rounding

19 • Order decimals.

42–44
121–124
• Round positive numbers to any given power of 10; round decimals to the nearest whole number or to one or two decimal places.

Integers, powers and roots

91, 92 • Add, subtract, multiply and divide integers.

135 • Recognise and use multiples, factors (divisors) and primes.

136, 137 • Use squares, square roots, cubes and index notation for small positive integer powers.

Fractions, decimals, percentages, ratio and proportion

23, 24 • Order fractions by writing them with a common denominator.

20,22
25,26
• Add and subtract fractions by writing them with a common denominator; calculate fractions of quantities (fraction answers); multiply an integer by a fraction.

27–29
34–39
• Interpret percentage as the operator 'so many hundredths of and express one given number as a percentage of another; use the equivalence of fractions, decimals and percentages to compare proportions; calculate percentages and find the outcome of a given percentage increase or decrease.

30–33
213
• Reduce a ratio to its simplest form, including a ratio expressed in different units, divide a quantity into two or more parts in a given ratio; use the unitary method to solve simple word problems involving ratio and direct proportion.

Calculations

Number operations and the relationships between them

91, 92 • Understand addition and subtraction of fractions and integers, and multiplication and division of integers.

90 • Use the order of operations, including brackets, with more complex calculations.

Mental methods and rapid recall of number facts

38, 39 • Recall known facts, including fraction to decimal conversions.

40, 41 • Consolidate and extend mental methods of calculation, working with decimals, fractions and percentages, squares and square roots, cubes; solve word problems mentally.

Written methods

125 • Consolidate standard column procedures for addition and subtraction of integers and decimals with up to two places.

126 • Use standard column procedures for multiplication and division of integers and decimals, understand where to position the decimal point by considering equivalent calculations.

Algebra

Equations, formulae and identities

45–47
204, 205
• Simplify or transform linear expressions by collecting like terms; multiply a single term over a bracket.

48 • Construct and solve linear equations with integer coefficients.

206 • Use formulae from mathematics and other subjects; substitute integers into simple formulae.

Sequences, functions and graphs

1, 2 • Generate and describe integer sequences.

3, 6 • Generate terms of a linear sequence using term-to-term and position-to-term definitions of the sequence.

3–6	• Begin to use linear expressions to describe the nth term of an arithmetic sequence.
7, 8	• Express simple functions in symbols; represent mappings expressed algebraically.
14–18 207, 208	• Generate points in all four quadrants and plot the graphs of linear functions, where y is given explicitly in terms of x.
9–13	• Construct linear functions arising from real-life problems and plot their corresponding graphs.

Shape, space and measures

Geometrical reasoning: lines, angles and shapes

55–60	• Identify alternate angles and corresponding angles; understand a proof that: – the sum of the angles of a triangle is 180° and of a quadrilateral is 360°.
62 214–216	• Classify quadrilaterals by their geometric properties.

Transformations

146, 147	• Transform 2-D shapes by simple combinations of rotations, reflections and translations, identify all the symmetries of 2-D shapes.
148–150	• Understand and use the language and notation associated with enlargement; enlarge 2-D shapes, given a centre of enlargement and a positive whole-number scale factor.
151–153	• Make simple scale drawings.

Coordinates

98–103	• Given the coordinates of points A and B, find the mid-point of the line segment AB.

Construction

68, 69, 70, 71	• Use straight edge and compasses to construct: – the mid-point and perpendicular bisector of a line segment; construct a triangle, given three sides (SSS).

Measures and mensuration

102–103 118–120 228–230	• Use units of measurement to estimate, calculate and solve problems in everyday contexts involving length, area, volume, capacity, mass, time, angle and bearings; know rough metric equivalents of imperial measures in daily use (feet, miles, pounds, pints, gallons).
228–230	• Use bearing to specify direction.
108–114	• Calculate areas of compound shapes made from rectangles and triangles.
115–117 226–227	• Know and use the formula for the volume of a cuboid; calculate volumes and surface areas of cuboids and shapes made from cuboids.

Handling data

Specifying a problem, planning and collecting data

84–86 217–219	• Decide which data to collect to answer a question, identify possible sources.
217–219	• Plan how to collect the data, construct frequency tables with given equal class intervals for sets of continuous data.
84–86	• Collect data using a suitable method, such as observation, controlled experiment, including data logging using ICT, or questionnaire.

Processing and representing data, using ICT as appropriate

79, 80 220–222	• Calculate statistics, including with a calculator; recognise when it is appropriate to use the range, mean, median and mode; construct and use stem-and-leaf diagrams.
75–78 217–219	• Construct, – pie charts – bar charts and frequency diagrams for discrete and continuous data.

Interpreting and discussing results

84–86 87–89 217–219	• Interpret tables, graphs and diagrams for both discrete and continuous data, and draw inferences that relate to the problem being discussed; relate summarised data to the questions being explored.
81–83	• Compare two distributions using the range and one or more of the mode, median and mean.
84–86 217–219	• Communicate orally and on paper the results of a statistical enquiry.

Probability

141, 143	• Know that if the probability of an event occurring is p, then the probability of it not occurring is 1 — p; find and record all possible mutually exclusive outcomes for single events and two successive events in a systematic way, using diagrams and tables.
144, 145	• Estimate probabilities from experimental data; understand that: – if an experiment is repeated there may be, and usually will be, different outcomes; – increasing the number of times an experiment is repeated generally leads to better estimates of probability.

Year 9 material
Number and the number system

Place value, ordering and rounding

121–124	• Use rounding to make estimates; round numbers to the nearest whole number or to one, two decimal places.

Fractions, decimals, percentages, ratio and proportion

154, 155	• Interpret and use ratio in a range of contexts, including solving word problems.

Calculations
Calculator methods

127–128	• Enter numbers and interpret the display in context (negative numbers, fractions, decimals, percentages, money, metric measures, time).

Algebra
Equations, formulae and identities

206	• Use formulae from mathematics and other subjects; substitute numbers into expressions and formulae.

Sequences, functions and graphs

3-6	• Generate sequences from practical contexts and write an expression to describe the nth term of an arithmetic sequence.

Shape, space and measures

Geometrical reasoning: lines, angles and shapes

Handling data

Specifying a problem, planning and collecting data

Sequences

On these pages you will look at number patterns and the rules to make patterns.

Ⓜ

① Copy and fill in the empty boxes for each Question.

(a) 2, 5, 8, ☐ 14, ☐   (g) 10 000, 2000, 400, ☐, ☐

(b) 3, 8, 13, ☐, 23, ☐   (h) 320, 160, 80, ☐, 20, ☐

(c) 3, 6, 9, ☐ 15, ☐   (i) 3, 6, 12, ☐, 48, ☐

(d) 2, 4, 6, ☐, 10, ☐   (j) –20, –18, –16, ☐, –12, ☐

(e) 25, 21, 17, ☐, 9, ☐   (k) ☐, –7, –4, ☐, 2, 5

(f) 50, 47, 44, ☐, 38, ☐   (l) 1, 3, 6, 10, ☐, 21, ☐

② For each sequence in Question ① above, write down the rule.
[example: a) add 3 each time].

③ Write the first five numbers of these sequences.

a) Start with 5 and add 4 each time

b) Start with 48 and subtract 6 each time

c) Start with 160 and divide by 2 each time

d) Start with –25 and add 6 each time

e) Start with 15 and subtract 4 each time

f) Start with 3 and multiply by 3 each time

g) Start with 1 000 000 and divide by 10 each time

h) Start with 81 and divide by 3 each time.

④ Use the given rule to copy and fill in the empty boxes for each sequence.

a) Rule: × 2 then add 4 ➡ Sequence: 2, 8, 20, ☐, ☐

b) Rule: × 3 then add 2 ➡ Sequence: 2, 8, 26, ☐, ☐

c) Rule: × 5 then subtract 2 ➡ Sequence: 1, 3, 13, ☐, ☐

d) Rule: × 4 then +2 ➡ Sequence: 3, 14, 58, ☐, ☐

e) Rule: × 2 then –3 ➡ Sequence: 4, 5, 7, ☐, ☐

f) Rule: × 4 then –6 ➡ Sequence: 2, 2, 2, ☐, ☐

2

E

For each question below, copy and complete the table of numbers. Use the diagrams to help.
The first question has been done for you.

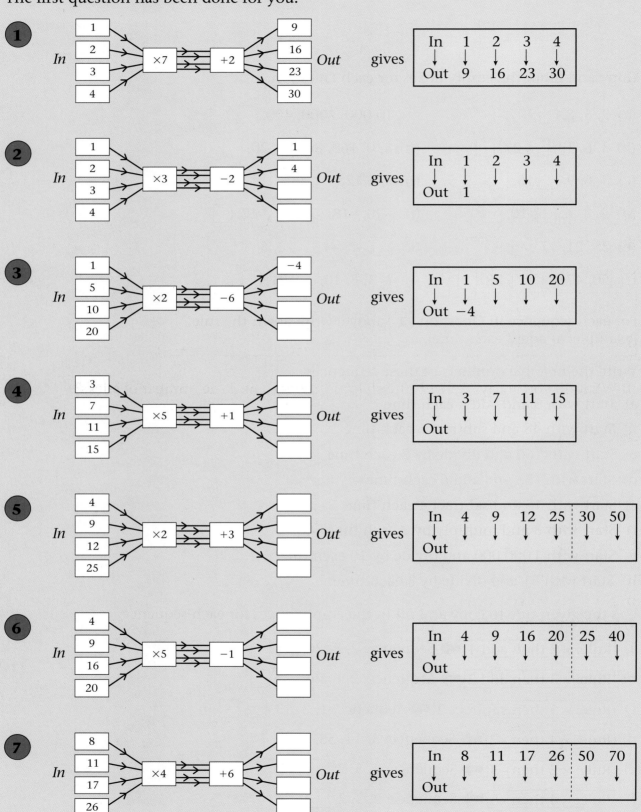

1 In ×7 +2 Out gives

In	1	2	3	4
Out	9	16	23	30

2 In ×3 −2 Out gives

In	1	2	3	4
Out	1			

3 In ×2 −6 Out gives

In	1	5	10	20
Out	−4			

4 In ×5 +1 Out gives

In	3	7	11	15
Out				

5 In ×2 +3 Out gives

In	4	9	12	25	30	50
Out						

6 In ×5 −1 Out gives

In	4	9	16	20	25	40
Out						

7 In ×4 +6 Out gives

In	8	11	17	26	50	70
Out						

Sequence rules

On these pages you will find the rules which fit patterns of numbers.

M

1 Shapes are made from matchsticks as follows:

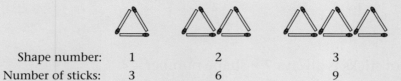

Shape number:	1	2	3
Number of sticks:	3	6	9

a) Draw the next 2 shapes.

b) How many extra sticks are needed each time?

c) Copy and complete this table:

Shape Number ↓	1	2	3	4	5	....	10	....	20
Number of sticks	3	6	9	□	□	....	□	....	□

d) What do you always do with the shape number to find the number of sticks?

2 Here is a sequence of shapes made from sticks.

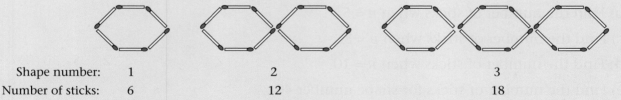

Shape number:	1	2	3
Number of sticks:	6	12	18

a) Draw the next shape.

b) How many extra sticks are needed each time?

c) Copy and complete the table:

Shape Number ↓	1	2	3	4	....	10
Number of sticks	6	12	18	□	....	□

d) What do you always do with the shape number to find the number of sticks?

e) Without drawing, how many sticks will you need for shape number 100?

4

③ Here is a sequence of shapes made from sticks.

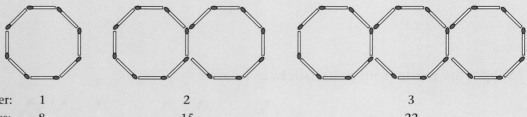

Shape number:	1	2	3
Number of sticks:	8	15	22

The number of sticks is always 7 × shape number + 1

We say the number of sticks = 7 × *n* + 1 where *n* is the shape number

We write

$$\text{number of sticks} = 7n + 1$$

Example

When $n = 2$, number of sticks $= 7n + 1 = 7 \times 2 + 1 = 15$

     (15 sticks for shape number 2)

When $n = 3$, number of sticks $= 7n + 1 = 7 \times 3 + 1 = 22$

     (22 sticks for shape number 3)

a) Find the number of sticks when $n = 4$ using $7n + 1$.

b) Find the number of sticks when $n = 5$.

c) Find the number of sticks when $n = 8$.

d) Find the number of sticks when $n = 10$.

e) Find the number of sticks for shape number 40.

In Questions **④** to **⑦** below, use the given rule to copy and complete each table.

④

Number of sticks = $2n + 5$

Shape number *n*	→	Number of sticks
1	→	7
2	→	
3	→	
4	→	
10	→	

⑤

Number of sticks = $3n + 10$

Shape number *n*	→	Number of sticks
1	→	
2	→	
3	→	
20	→	
50	→	

6

Number of sticks = $5n - 2$	
Shape number n $\longrightarrow$	Number of sticks
1 $\longrightarrow$	
2 $\longrightarrow$	
3 $\longrightarrow$	
10 $\longrightarrow$	
20 $\longrightarrow$	

7

Number of sticks = $8n - 3$	
Shape number n $\longrightarrow$	Number of sticks
1 $\longrightarrow$	
2 $\longrightarrow$	
3 $\longrightarrow$	
50 $\longrightarrow$	
80 $\longrightarrow$	

E

1 For each value of n, find the value of $3n + 4$ in the table below (copy the table).

n	1	2	3	4	10	20
$3n + 4$	7	10				

2 For each value of n, find the value of $2n - 1$ in the table below (copy the table).

n	1	2	3	4	10	20
$2n - 1$	1	3				

3 For each value of n, find the value of $4n + 5$ in the table below (copy the table).

n	1	2	3	4	8	50
$4n + 5$	9					

4 For each value of n, find the value of $6n - 5$ in the table below (copy the table).

n	1	2	3	10	20	50
$6n - 5$						

5 Copy and complete the table below.

n	1	2	3	5	20	100
$10n - 2$						

Example

A sequence of shapes is made from sticks.
The number of sticks needed for each shape number is shown in this table.

Shape number n		Number of sticks
1	$\longrightarrow$	4
2	$\longrightarrow$	7
3	$\longrightarrow$	10
4	$\longrightarrow$	13

> Find the rule for the number of sticks for shape number n.

Look at the number of sticks 4, 7, 10, 13.
The difference between the numbers is 3.

If all the differences are the *same*, there will be 2 parts to the rule, starting with $\boxed{\times 3}$.

The second part will be $\boxed{+?}$ or $\boxed{-?}$ to make the rule work.

In this case $\boxed{\times 3}$ $\boxed{+1}$ so start with shape number n then $\boxed{\times 3}$ and $\boxed{+1}$.

Number of sticks = $n \times 3 + 1$.

We say | number of sticks = $3n + 1$ |.

Test the rule with different n numbers to make sure it works.

In Questions ⑥ to ⑪, for each table find the rule for the number of sticks for shape number n.

6

Shape number n		Number of sticks
1	$\longrightarrow$	7
2	$\longrightarrow$	9
3	$\longrightarrow$	11
4	$\longrightarrow$	13

8

Shape number n		Number of sticks
1	$\longrightarrow$	6
2	$\longrightarrow$	11
3	$\longrightarrow$	16
4	$\longrightarrow$	21

10

Shape number n		Number of sticks
1	$\longrightarrow$	9
2	$\longrightarrow$	16
3	$\longrightarrow$	23
4	$\longrightarrow$	30

7

Shape number n		Number of sticks
1	$\longrightarrow$	2
2	$\longrightarrow$	5
3	$\longrightarrow$	8
4	$\longrightarrow$	11

9

Shape number n		Number of sticks
1	$\longrightarrow$	2
2	$\longrightarrow$	6
3	$\longrightarrow$	10
4	$\longrightarrow$	14

11

Shape number n		Number of sticks
1	$\longrightarrow$	9
2	$\longrightarrow$	16
3	$\longrightarrow$	23
4	$\longrightarrow$	30

Using words for functions

On these pages you will use words to describe algebraic expressions.

Start with a number *n*.

Multiply the number by 2 then add 3.

What is the answer?

Using algebra,

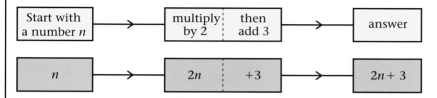

The answer 2*n* + 3 is called an algebraic expression.

Example

Write in words what is happening below:

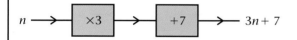

$n \longrightarrow \boxed{\times 3} \longrightarrow \boxed{+7} \longrightarrow 3n + 7$

Answer

Start with a number *n*.

Multiply the number by 3 then add 7.

The answer is 3*n* + 7.

M

For each Question below, write in words what is happening (like the example above).

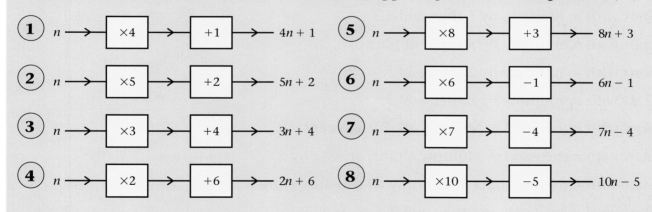

(1) $n \longrightarrow \boxed{\times 4} \longrightarrow \boxed{+1} \longrightarrow 4n + 1$

(5) $n \longrightarrow \boxed{\times 8} \longrightarrow \boxed{+3} \longrightarrow 8n + 3$

(2) $n \longrightarrow \boxed{\times 5} \longrightarrow \boxed{+2} \longrightarrow 5n + 2$

(6) $n \longrightarrow \boxed{\times 6} \longrightarrow \boxed{-1} \longrightarrow 6n - 1$

(3) $n \longrightarrow \boxed{\times 3} \longrightarrow \boxed{+4} \longrightarrow 3n + 4$

(7) $n \longrightarrow \boxed{\times 7} \longrightarrow \boxed{-4} \longrightarrow 7n - 4$

(4) $n \longrightarrow \boxed{\times 2} \longrightarrow \boxed{+6} \longrightarrow 2n + 6$

(8) $n \longrightarrow \boxed{\times 10} \longrightarrow \boxed{-5} \longrightarrow 10n - 5$

In Questions **(9)** to **(17)**, write in words how you get the algebraic expression.

(Question **(9)** is done for you.)

(9) 2*n* + 10

Answer:

Start with a number *n*. Multiply the number by 2 then add 10. The answer is 2*n* + 10.

(10) 6*n* + 14

(12) 5*n* – 12

(14) 3*n* + 20

(16) 14*n* – 6

(11) 3*n* – 5

(13) 7*n* + 11

(15) 10*n* – 2

(17) 11*n* + 1

Example

Write in words what is happening below:

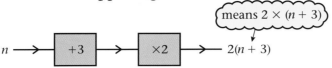

means 2 × (n + 3)

n → +3 → ×2 → 2(n + 3)

Answer

Start with a number *n*. Add 3.
Multiply all this answer by 2.
The answer is 2(*n* + 3).

E

For each Question below, write in words what is happening.

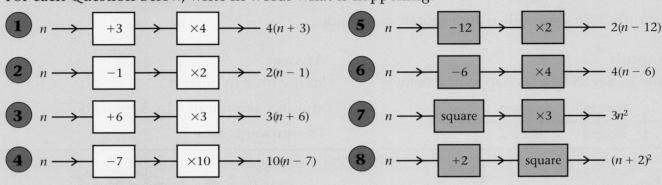

1 n → +3 → ×4 → 4(n + 3)

2 n → −1 → ×2 → 2(n − 1)

3 n → +6 → ×3 → 3(n + 6)

4 n → −7 → ×10 → 10(n − 7)

5 n → −12 → ×2 → 2(n − 12)

6 n → −6 → ×4 → 4(n − 6)

7 n → square → ×3 → 3n²

8 n → +2 → square → (n + 2)²

In Questions **9** to **16**, write down the answer you get (i.e. the algebraic expression).

9 Start with *n*, multiply by 5 then add 8.

10 Start with *n*, multiply by 6 then subtract 3.

11 Start with *n*, multiply by 2 then add *b*.

12 Start with *n*, multiply by 8 then add 7.

13 Start with *n* then add 4. Multiply all this answer by 6.

14 Start with *n* then add 9. Multiply all this answer by 3.

15 Start with *n* then subtract 8. Multiply all this answer by 5.

16 Start with *n*, square it and then add 2.

In Questions **17** to **25**, write in words how you get the algebraic expression.

(Question **17** is done for you.)

17 $3(n + 2)$

Answer:

Start with a number n then add 2. Multiply all this answer by 3. The answer is $3(n + 2)$.

18 $6(n + 5)$ **20** $3n − 12$ **22** $6n + 9$ **24** $n^2 − 7$

19 $4(n − 1)$ **21** $5(n − 3)$ **23** $2(n + 4)$ **25** $(n + 3)^2$

On these pages you will read from graphs and draw graphs from real-life events.

M

1. In 1971 Britain changed from its old money to a new one. 240 old pennies became 100 new pence.

   This graph converts old pennies to new pence.

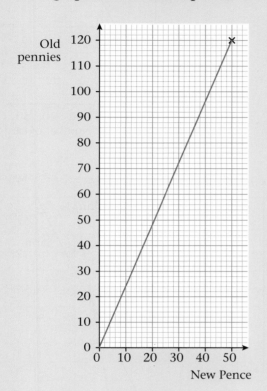

a) How many old pennies is today's 50p worth?

b) How many old pennies is today's 25p worth?

c) How many new pence are 84 old pennies worth?

d) How many new pence are 72 old pennies worth?

e) How many new pence are 24 old pennies worth?

f) How many new pence are 96 old pennies worth?

Before the change, 12 old pennies were called a shilling.
How many new pence would you get for

g) 1 shilling   h) 5 shillings   i) 10 shillings?

2 A pack of 50 playing cards is 40 mm high.
Use the graph to answer the questions below.
How many cards are there in a pile

a) 16 mm high?

b) 24 mm high?

c) 32 mm high?

d) 28 mm high?

e) What does one small square on the 'number of cards' axis show.

How high would the pile be if it had

f) 25 cards   h) 35 cards

g) 45 cards   i) 5 cards?

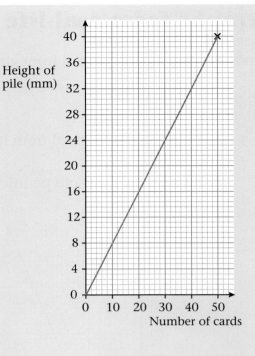

3 Sarita and John decided to go for a swim at the leisure centre 6 miles from where they lived.

Sarita set out at noon and walked at a steady speed. John set off later on his bike.

Their journey is shown on the graph.

a) When did John set off?

b) How long did Sarita take to get to the leisure centre?

c) When did John overtake Sarita?

d) How far had John travelled when he overtook Sarita?

e) How long did it take John to reach the leisure centre?

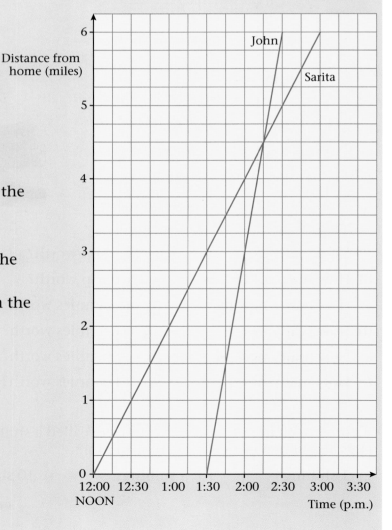

4 At midnight a helicopter flew out to sea to rescue the crew of a ship and had to make two trips.

This is shown on the graph.

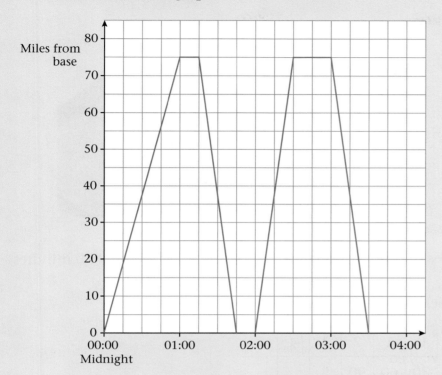

a) What length of time is shown by one square?

On the first visit to the ship,

b) how long did it take the pilot to reach the ship?

c) how long was it over the ship?

d) when did it get back to base?

On the second visit to the ship,

e) how long did the pilot take to reach the ship?

f) how long was it over the ship?

g) how long was its return trip?

h) when did it arrive back at base?

1 Draw the axes below:

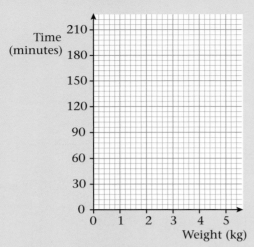

A recipe for cooking roast-beef says 'cook for 30 minutes per kilogram and add 30 minutes extra'.

Copy and complete the table below:

Weight of beef (kg)	0	1	2	3	4	5
Cooking time (minutes)	30	60	90			

Plot these points on the graph and join them up to make a straight line (use a ruler).

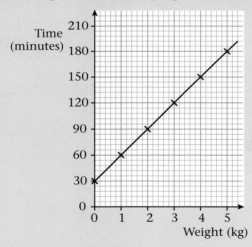

Use your graph to answer the questions below:

a) What does one small square on the time axis show you?

How long should you cook a piece of beef weighing:

b) 1.5 kg   c) 2.5 kg   d) 4.5 kg?

What weight of beef should be cooked for:

e) 75 minutes   f) 135 minutes   g) 45 minutes   h) $2\frac{1}{2}$ hours?

Example

The journey below is shown on the travel graph.
At 13:00 Dan leaves his home and cycles 10 km
at a steady speed for 1 hour. He stays for $\frac{1}{2}$ hour.
He cycles another 15 km in 1 hour. He then returns
home in $1\frac{1}{2}$ hours.

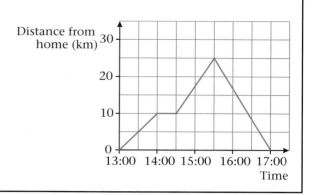

In Questions ② to ④ below, copy the axes then draw a travel graph to show each journey.

②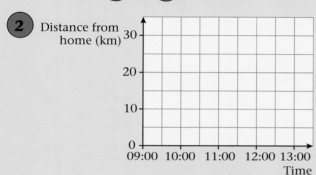

Jo leaves her home at 09:00.

She cycles 15 km at a steady speed for
1 hour. She stops for 1 hour.

She cycles another 5 km in $\frac{1}{2}$ hour.

She then returns home in $1\frac{1}{2}$ hours.

③ Suzy leaves home at 12:00 on her horse and
rides 20 km at a steady *speed* for 1 hour.

Suzy and her horse then rest for 45 minutes
and afterwards travel another 15 km in
45 minutes.

Suzy and her horse then return home in $1\frac{1}{2}$ hours.

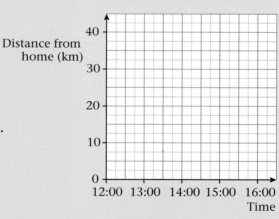

④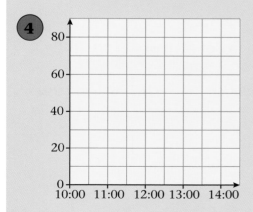

At 10:00 Mr. Toms leaves home and drives 50 km in
1 hour at a steady speed. He stops at a Service

Station for $\frac{1}{2}$ hour. He travels another 30 km

in $\frac{1}{2}$ hour. He then stops for $\frac{1}{2}$ hour before returning

home in $1\frac{1}{2}$ hours.

On these pages you will use and draw straight line graphs.

Ⓜ

① a) Write down the co-ordinates for each of the points A, B, C, D, E.

b) Write down the letter given by each co-ordinate below to make two words.

(−5, 2) (1, 1) (2, 4) (−5, −2)
(−3, −2) (4, −2) (5, −3)
(−5, −3) (−3, 4)

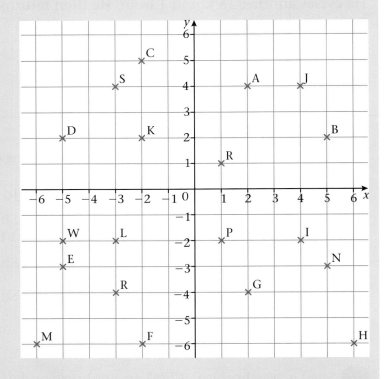

②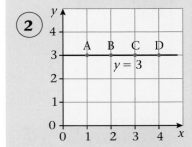

At point A, y = 3
At point B, y = 3
At point B, y = 3
At point B, y = 3
All the points lie on a straight line.

The y-co-ordinate of all the points is 3 so we say the *equation* of the line is y = 3.

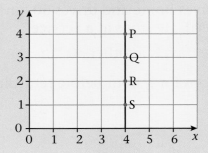

a) Write down the co-ordinates of each of the points P, Q, R and S.

b) Write down a *sensible equation* for the line which passes through P, Q, R and S.

3 Write down the equations of the lines marked A, B and C.

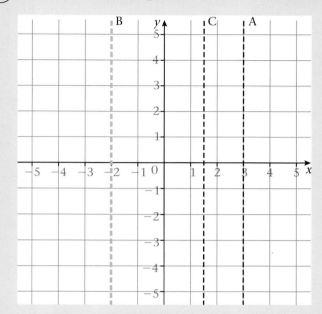

4

Write down the co-ordinates for each point.

A (2, 3)   G (,)

B (,)   H (,)

C (,)   I (,)

D (,)   J (,)

E (,)   K (,)

F (,)   L (,)

5 Letter A lies on the line $y = 3$. Which other letter lies on $y = 3$?

6 Which letter lies on $y = -4$?

7 K lies on the line $x = -2$. Which other letter lies on $x = -2$?

8 Which letters lie on $x = 1$?

9 What letter lies on $x = 3$ and $y = -1$?

10 Copy this graph.

    a) Draw the line $x = 2$.

    b) Draw the line $y = -3$.

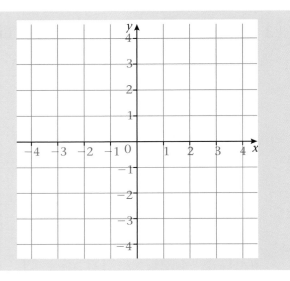

Example

Draw the graph of $y = 2x + 1$. Use x-values from 0 to 4.

Answer

Use x-values: 0, 1, 2, 3, 4

Use $y = 2x + 1$ to find y-values which belong to each x-value.

When $x = 0$, $y = 2x + 1$ means $y = 2 \times x + 1 = 2 \times 0 + 1 = 0 + 1 = 1$

put in equation

so one point is $x = 0,\ y = 1$ (0, 1)

When $x = 1$, $y = 2x + 1$ means $y = 2 \times 1 + 1 = 2 + 1 = 3$

so one point is $x = 1,\ y = 3$ (1, 3)

When $x = 2$, $y = 2 \times 2 + 1 = 4 + 1 = 5$ (2, 5)
When $x = 3$, $y = 2 \times 3 + 1 = 6 + 1 = 7$ (3, 7)
When $x = 4$, $y = 2 \times 4 + 1 = 8 + 1 = 9$ (4, 9)

Draw axes, plot the 5 points and
join them up to make a straight line.

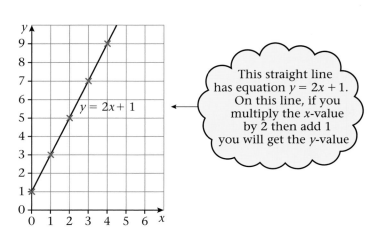

This straight line
has equation $y = 2x + 1$.
On this line, if you
multiply the x-value
by 2 then add 1
you will get the y-value

E

1 The equation of a line is $y = 2x + 3$.

Copy and complete this list of co-ordinates

$x = 0$, $y = 2x + 3 = 2 \times 0 + 3 = 3$ $(0, 3)$

$x = 1$, $y = 2 \times 1 + 3 = 5$ $(1, 5)$

$x = 2$, $y = \ldots\ldots = \Box$ $(2, \Box)$

$x = 3$, $y = \ldots\ldots = \Box$ $(3, \Box)$

$x = 4$, $y = \ldots\ldots = \Box$ $(4, \Box)$

Draw these axes on squared paper.

Plot the 5 points above.

Join up the points to make a straight line.

The equation of this line is $y = 2x + 3$.

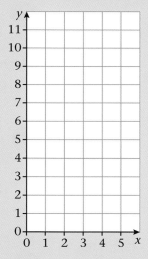

2 The equation of a line is $y = 8 - x$.

Copy and complete this list of co-ordinates.

$x = 0$, $y = 8 - 0 = 8$ $(0, 8)$

$x = 1$, $y = 8 - 1 = 7$ $(1, 7)$

$x = 2$, $y = \ldots\ldots = \Box$ $(2, \Box)$

$x = 3$, $y = \ldots\ldots = \Box$ $(3, \Box)$

$x = 4$, $y = \ldots\ldots = \Box$ $(4, \Box)$

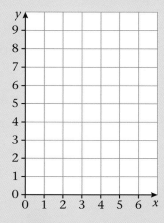

On squared paper, draw an x-axis from 0 to 6 and a y-axis from 0 to 9 as shown.

Plot the 5 points from above. Join up these points to make a straight line.

The equation of this straight line is $y = 8 - x$.

3 The equation of a line is $y = 2x + 1$

Copy and complete this list of co-ordinates,

$x = 0$, $y = 2 \times 0 + 1 = 1$ $(0, 1)$

$x = 1$, $y = 2 \times 1 + 1 = 3$ $(1, 3)$

$x = 2$, $y = \ldots\ldots = \Box$ $(2, \Box)$

$x = 3$, $y = \ldots\ldots = \Box$ $(3, \Box)$

$x = 4$, $y = \ldots\ldots = \Box$ $(4, \Box)$

On squared paper, draw an x-axis from 0 to 5 and a y-axis from 0 to 11 as shown in question **1**.

Plot the 5 points from above. Join up these points to make a straight line. The equation of this straight line is $y = 2x + 1$.

For each Question you will need to draw axes like these:

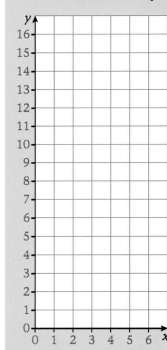

4 $y = 2x + 5$

Complete the co-ordinates:

(0, 5) (1, 7) (2, ☐)(3, ☐),(4, ☐)

Plot these points and draw the graph.

5 $y = 3x + 3$

Complete the co-ordinates:

(0, 3) (1, 6) (2, ☐) (3, ☐) (4, ☐)

Plot these points and draw the graph.

6 $y = 9 - x$

Complete the co-ordinates:

(0, 9) (1, 8) (2, ☐) (3, ☐) (4, ☐)

Plot these points and draw the graph.

7 $y = 3x - 1$

Complete the co-ordinates:

(1, 2) (2, 5) (3, ☐)(4, ☐)(5, ☐)

Draw the graph.

8 $y = 12 - x$

Complete the co-ordinates:

(0, 12) (1, 11) (2, ☐) (3, ☐), (4, ☐)

Draw the graph.

9 $y = 4x - 3$

Complete the co-ordinates:

(1, 1) (2, ☐)(3, ☐)(4, ☐) Draw the graph.

Note

Check all your graphs with a computer or graphical calculator if your teacher wants you to!

On this page you will learn to order a set of decimals.

> Write the set of decimals in a line with the decimal points in a column.
> Fill in any empty spaces with zeros. This makes it easier to compare the decimals.
>
> **Example**   Arrange 5.3, 0.35, 8 and 5.8 in order.
>
> | Write in column. | Put in zeros. | Arrange in order. |
> |---|---|---|
> | 5.3 | 5.30 | 0.35 |
> | 0.35 | 0.35 | 5.3 |
> | 8 | 8.00 | 5.8 |
> | 5.8 | 5.80 | 8 |

M

Write the larger of these pairs of numbers.

1. 1.7   7.0   **4.** 21   2.1   **7.** 7.0   3.7   **10.** 5.4   4.5
2. 35   5.3   **5.** 1.0   1.1   **8.** 0.3   3.0   **11.** 7.5   57
3. 4.0   2.4   **6.** 2.5   25   **9.** 8.0   6.8   **12.** 1.5   5.0

13. Copy the number line. Put each number from the box on the line.

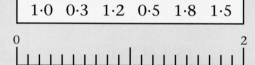

| 1·0   0·3   1·2   0·5   1·8   1·5 |

Arrange these decimals in order. Write the smallest first.

14. 5.62, 6.52, 5.26, 6.5, 6.25

15. 3.18, 1.8, 3.81, 3.8, 1.38

16. 6.76, 6.6, 6.06, 6.7, 6.07

17. 21.8, 2.8, 2.18, 2.08, 28

18. Copy the line and locate the numbers.

| 2·95 3·06 3·0 2·91 2·98 3·04 |

E

Arrange these decimals in order. Write the smallest first.

1. 4.2, 4.25, 0.45, 4.5, 4.52   **5.** 11.7, 1.71, 17.1, 1.17, 1.7
2. 6.1, 6.71, 0.67, 6.7, 6.17   **6.** 3.66, 3.36, 33.3, 3.63, 3.33
3. 3.39, 0.93, 3.09, 0.39, 3.3   **7.** 2.52, 2.2, 25.2, 22.5, 2.25
4. 8.4, 8.22, 8.24, 8.44, 8.42   **8.** 4.64, 4.646, 4.66, 4.646, 4.644

On these pages you will learn to find a fraction of a number or quantity.

Examples

$\frac{1}{9}$ of 36 = 36 ÷ 9 $\frac{1}{7}$ of 154 = 154 ÷ 7

       = 4

$$\begin{array}{r} 2\,2 \\ 7\overline{)15^14} \end{array}$$

Answer: 22

$\frac{2}{3}$ of 24 = (24 ÷ 3) × 2 $\frac{7}{10}$ of 80 = (80 ÷ 10) × 7

      = 8 × 2 = 16   = 8 × 7 = 56

Ⓜ   Part One

Find $\frac{1}{3}$ of:

(1) 18   **(3)** 27   **(5)** 33 cm   **(7)** 21p

(2) 12   **(4)** 30   **(6)** 6p   **(8)** 36 cm

Find $\frac{1}{7}$ of:

(9) 21   **(14)** 49p   **(19)** $\frac{1}{6}$ of 54p   **(24)** $\frac{1}{10}$ of 140 cm

(10) 35   **(15)** 28 cm   **(20)** $\frac{1}{8}$ of 40 cm   **(25)** $\frac{1}{5}$ of 55 cm

(11) 42   **(16)** 77 cm   **(21)** $\frac{1}{9}$ of 45 kg   **(26)** $\frac{1}{5}$ of 75 ml

(12) 63   **(17)** $\frac{1}{4}$ of 32   **(22)** $\frac{1}{8}$ of 56 kg   **(27)** $\frac{1}{10}$ of 320 ml

(13) 14p   **(18)** $\frac{1}{6}$ of 30p   **(23)** $\frac{1}{9}$ of 72p   **(28)** $\frac{1}{8}$ of 48p

(29) Marvin had collected £720 for charities.

     He gave $\frac{1}{6}$ of the money to a Cancer charity.

     How much money did he give to the Cancer charity?

(30) Sally had 90 CDs. She gave Terry $\frac{1}{3}$ of her CDs.

     Ron had 128 CDs. He gave Chloe $\frac{1}{4}$ of his CDs.

     Who had more CDs, Terry or Chloe?

In Questions **(31)** and **(32)**, copy and fill in the empty box.

(31) $\frac{1}{3}$ of 30 = $\frac{1}{4}$ of ☐

(32) $\frac{1}{5}$ of 60 = $\frac{1}{4}$ of ☐

Ⓜ Part Two

Find $\frac{2}{5}$ of: Find $\frac{3}{8}$ of:

① 30   ③ 40p   ⑤ 24   ⑦ 72p

② 45   ④ 100   ⑥ 40   ⑧ 64 cm

Work out:

⑨ $\frac{5}{8}$ of £48   ⑬ $\frac{3}{10}$ of 280 cm   ⑰ $\frac{5}{6}$ of 54 kg

⑩ $\frac{4}{7}$ of £63   ⑭ $\frac{4}{9}$ of 72 cm   ⑱ $\frac{3}{7}$ of 84 km

⑪ $\frac{6}{9}$ of £180   ⑮ $\frac{1}{7}$ of 189 cm   ⑲ $\frac{9}{10}$ of 360 km

⑫ $\frac{2}{3}$ of £210   ⑯ $\frac{1}{9}$ of 315 kg   ⑳ $\frac{5}{9}$ of 54 p

㉑ A can of coke contains 330 ml. Ceri drinks $\frac{2}{3}$ of the can.

How much coke is left in the can?

Example

Work out $\frac{3}{5} \times 35$

Answer: $\frac{3}{5} \times 35$ means $\frac{3}{5}$ of 35

$= (35 \div 5) \times 3$

$= 7 \times 3 = 21$

> 'of' means '×'
>
> $\frac{3}{7}$ of 28 can be written $\frac{3}{7} \times 28$

Your teacher may wish to teach you the 'cancelling' way.

Sometimes it is easier to work out multiplication by cancelling.

Method: (i) Multiply the numbers on the top

(ii) Multiply the numbers on the bottom

(iii) Cancel down if necessary. This can be done either before or after multiplying.

a) $\frac{2}{3} \times \frac{5}{7} = \frac{10}{21}$

b) $\frac{3}{4} \times 12$

$= \frac{3}{\cancel{4}_1} \times \frac{\cancel{12}^3}{1}$

$= \frac{9}{1} = 9$

c) $\frac{^1\cancel{5}}{\cancel{8}_1} \times \frac{\cancel{16}^2}{\cancel{25}_5}$

$= \frac{2}{5}$

E

Work out

1 $\frac{1}{4} \times 8$

2 $\frac{1}{3} \times 45$

3 $\frac{1}{2} \times 30$

4 $\frac{1}{3} \times 24$

5 $\frac{1}{4} \times 80$

6 $\frac{2}{3} \times \frac{1}{5}$

7 $\frac{3}{5} \times \frac{3}{4}$

8 $\frac{5}{7} \times \frac{3}{4}$

9 $\frac{2}{5} \times \frac{3}{7}$

Copy and complete the following questions:

10 $\frac{3}{8} \times 16 = \frac{3}{\overset{}{\underset{1}{8}}} \times \frac{\overset{2}{16}}{1} = \frac{\square}{\square} = \square$

11 $\frac{4}{7} \times 28 = \frac{4}{\overset{}{\underset{1}{7}}} \times \frac{\overset{4}{28}}{1} = \frac{\square}{\square} = \square$

12 $\frac{5}{\overset{}{\underset{1}{9}}} \times \frac{\overset{5}{45}}{1} = \frac{\square}{\square} = \square$

13 $\frac{5}{\overset{}{\underset{1}{12}}} \times \frac{\overset{3}{36}}{1} = \frac{\square}{\square} = \square$

14 $\frac{4}{\overset{}{\underset{3}{15}}} \times \frac{\overset{1}{5}}{7} = \frac{\square}{\square}$

15 $\frac{\overset{1}{4}}{5} \times \frac{7}{\overset{}{\underset{2}{8}}} = \frac{\square}{\square}$

Work out, using cancelling:

16 $\frac{3}{8} \times \frac{4}{5}$

17 $\frac{5}{9} \times \frac{3}{4}$

18 $\frac{2}{9} \times \frac{6}{7}$

19 $\frac{2}{3} \times 6$

20 $\frac{3}{14} \times \frac{7}{10}$

21 $\frac{5}{6} \times 18$

22 $\frac{7}{10} \times 50$

23 $\frac{5}{8} \times \frac{6}{15}$

Work out

24 $\frac{2}{3}$ of 12

25 $\frac{3}{4}$ of 20

26 $\frac{1}{5}$ of $\frac{2}{3}$

27 $\frac{2}{7}$ of $\frac{1}{2}$

28 The petrol tank of a mower holds $\frac{1}{2}$ litre.

How much petrol is in the tank when it is $\frac{3}{5}$ full?

29 Answer true or false:

a) $\frac{1}{2}$ of $7 = \frac{7}{2}$ b) $\frac{1}{5}$ of $20 = 20 \div \frac{1}{5}$ c) $\frac{2}{3}$ of $\frac{1}{3} = \frac{2}{9}$

30 Find the odd one out:

a) $\frac{1}{3}$ of 36   b) $\frac{3}{4}$ of 20   c) $\frac{3}{8} \times 32$

Ordering Fractions

On these pages you will use equivalent fractions to order fractions.

A fraction can be changed to an equivalent fraction by:

CANCELLING	MULTIPLYING
Example	Example
$\dfrac{8}{12} \dfrac{(\div 4)}{(\div 4)} = \dfrac{2}{3}$	$\dfrac{5}{8} \dfrac{(\times 3)}{(\times 3)} = \dfrac{15}{24}$

In Questions **1** to **4**, are the fractions *equivalent*?

1
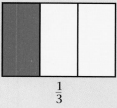

$\dfrac{1}{3}$ $\dfrac{4}{12}$

3
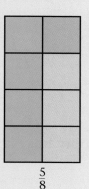

$\dfrac{5}{8}$ $\dfrac{9}{16}$

2
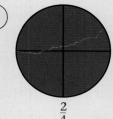

$\dfrac{2}{4}$ $\dfrac{3}{8}$

4
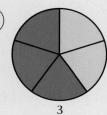

$\dfrac{3}{5}$ $\dfrac{6}{10}$

In Questions **5** to **14**, copy and complete the equivalent fractions.

5 $\dfrac{3}{4} = \dfrac{\square}{20}$ **8** $\dfrac{2}{5} = \dfrac{8}{\square}$ **11** $\dfrac{20}{30} = \dfrac{\square}{3}$ **14** $\dfrac{3}{8} = \dfrac{\square}{48}$

6 $\dfrac{5}{7} = \dfrac{\square}{42}$ **9** $\dfrac{5}{6} = \dfrac{15}{\square}$ **12** $\dfrac{16}{24} = \dfrac{2}{\square}$

7 $\dfrac{1}{3} = \dfrac{\square}{18}$ **10** $\dfrac{4}{9} = \dfrac{\square}{54}$ **13** $\dfrac{25}{30} = \dfrac{5}{\square}$

In Questions **15** to **24**, cancel each fraction into its *simplest form*:

15 $\dfrac{6}{10}$ **17** $\dfrac{8}{20}$ **19** $\dfrac{15}{35}$ **21** $\dfrac{12}{36}$ **23** $\dfrac{10}{32}$

16 $\dfrac{5}{20}$ **18** $\dfrac{4}{12}$ **20** $\dfrac{16}{24}$ **22** $\dfrac{28}{64}$ **24** $\dfrac{56}{72}$

Example

Arrange $\frac{7}{20}$, $\frac{1}{2}$, $\frac{3}{10}$ in order, starting with the smallest fraction.

You MUST make the denominator (bottom number) the same for each fraction so that you can see which is the smallest fraction.

20, 2 and 10 all divide into 20 so use 20 as the *common denominator*.

we have   Answer:

$$\frac{7}{\boxed{20}} \qquad \frac{1}{2} = \frac{10}{\boxed{20}} \qquad \frac{3}{10} = \frac{6}{\boxed{20}} \qquad\qquad \frac{3}{10}, \ \frac{7}{20}, \ \frac{1}{2}$$

E

1 Copy and fill in the empty boxes below to arrange $\frac{2}{3}$, $\frac{7}{12}$, $\frac{3}{4}$ in order, starting with the smallest fraction.

$$\frac{2}{3} = \frac{\square}{12} \qquad\qquad \frac{7}{12} \qquad\qquad \frac{3}{4} = \frac{\square}{12}$$

Answer: $\dfrac{\square}{\square}$, $\dfrac{\square}{\square}$, $\dfrac{\square}{\square}$

2 Copy and fill in the empty boxes below to arrange $\frac{7}{8}$, $\frac{13}{16}$, $\frac{3}{4}$ in order, starting with the smallest fraction.

$$\frac{7}{8} = \frac{\square}{16} \qquad\qquad \frac{13}{16} \qquad\qquad \frac{3}{4} = \frac{\square}{16}$$

Answer: $\dfrac{\square}{\square}$, $\dfrac{\square}{\square}$, $\dfrac{\square}{\square}$

3 Copy and fill in the empty boxes below to arrange $\frac{2}{3}$, $\frac{3}{5}$, $\frac{7}{10}$, $\frac{8}{15}$ in order, starting with the smallest fraction

$$\frac{2}{3} = \frac{\square}{30} \qquad \frac{3}{5} = \frac{\square}{30} \qquad \frac{7}{10} = \frac{\square}{30} \qquad \frac{8}{15} = \frac{\square}{30}$$

Answer: $\dfrac{\square}{\square}$, $\dfrac{\square}{\square}$, $\dfrac{\square}{\square}$, $\dfrac{\square}{\square}$

4 Write down the smaller fraction:

a) $\frac{1}{5}$ or $\frac{1}{6}$ b) $\frac{2}{3}$ or $\frac{2}{5}$ c) $\frac{3}{4}$ or $\frac{4}{7}$

In Questions **5** to **10**, place the fractions in order, starting with the smallest.

5 $\frac{1}{3}$, $\frac{1}{4}$, $\frac{1}{6}$ **7** $\frac{5}{8}$, $\frac{1}{2}$, $\frac{7}{16}$, $\frac{3}{4}$ **9** $1\frac{4}{15}$, $1\frac{1}{3}$, $1\frac{3}{10}$, $2\frac{1}{10}$

6 $\frac{7}{10}$, $\frac{4}{5}$, $\frac{15}{20}$ **8** $\frac{2}{3}$, $\frac{5}{6}$, $\frac{4}{9}$, $\frac{2}{4}$ **10** $2\frac{3}{4}$, $2\frac{7}{12}$, $2\frac{5}{6}$, $2\frac{1}{2}$

Adding and Subtracting Fractions

On these pages you will add and subtract fractions.

Remember:

Fractions can be added or subtracted when they have the same denominator (bottom number).

Examples

$$\frac{3}{5} + \frac{1}{5} = \frac{4}{5} \qquad \frac{6}{7} - \frac{2}{7} = \frac{4}{7}$$

never add the denominators

Sometimes the denominators have to be made the same before adding or subtracting. Use equivalent fractions.

Examples

(a) $\frac{1}{5} + \frac{1}{3}$

Denominator 15 chosen because both 5 and 3 divide into 15

$= \frac{3}{15} + \frac{5}{15}$

$= \frac{8}{15}$

(b) $\frac{5}{6} - \frac{2}{9}$

Denominator 18 chosen because both 6 and 9 divide into 18

$= \frac{15}{18} - \frac{4}{18}$

$= \frac{11}{18}$

Ⓜ

Work out

1 $\frac{3}{8} + \frac{2}{8}$

2 $\frac{5}{7} + \frac{1}{7}$

3 $\frac{2}{7} + \frac{3}{7}$

4 $\frac{2}{5} + \frac{2}{5}$

5 $\frac{8}{9} - \frac{4}{9}$

6 $\frac{7}{11} - \frac{2}{11}$

7 $\frac{6}{13} - \frac{3}{13}$

8 $\frac{2}{9} + \frac{5}{9}$

9 $\frac{8}{19} - \frac{5}{19}$

Work out

10 $\frac{6}{9} + \frac{1}{9} + \frac{1}{9}$

11 $\frac{5}{13} + \frac{6}{13} - \frac{4}{13}$

12 $\frac{8}{11} + \frac{2}{11} - \frac{5}{11}$

13 $\frac{3}{7} + \frac{1}{7} + \frac{2}{7} - \frac{4}{7}$

In questions ⑭ and ⑮, which answer is the odd one out?

14 (a) $\frac{5}{7} + \frac{1}{7}$ (b) $\frac{3}{7} + \frac{3}{7}$ (c) $\frac{4}{7} + \frac{1}{7}$

15 (a) $\frac{10}{11} - \frac{3}{11}$ (b) $\frac{5}{11} + \frac{2}{11}$ (c) $\frac{8}{11} - \frac{2}{11}$

16 Ally sleeps for $\frac{4}{12}$ of the day and works for $\frac{5}{12}$ of the day.

What total fraction of the day does Ally sleep and work?

E

1 Copy and complete these calculations:

a) $\dfrac{1}{4} + \dfrac{3}{5}$

$= \dfrac{\square}{20} + \dfrac{\square}{20}$

$= \dfrac{\square}{20}$

b) $\dfrac{2}{9} + \dfrac{3}{7}$

$= \dfrac{\square}{63} + \dfrac{\square}{63}$

$= \dfrac{\square}{63}$

(c) $\dfrac{5}{8} - \dfrac{1}{4}$

$= \dfrac{\square}{8} - \dfrac{\square}{8}$

$= \dfrac{\square}{8}$

2 Copy and complete these calculations:

a) $\dfrac{3}{7} + \dfrac{2}{5}$

$= \dfrac{\square}{35} + \dfrac{\square}{35}$

$= \dfrac{\square}{35}$

b) $\dfrac{6}{7} - \dfrac{5}{6}$

$= \dfrac{\square}{42} - \dfrac{\square}{42}$

$= \dfrac{\square}{42}$

c) $\dfrac{7}{8} - \dfrac{2}{3}$

$= \dfrac{\square}{24} - \dfrac{\square}{24}$

$= \dfrac{\square}{24}$

3 Work out

a) $\dfrac{2}{7} + \dfrac{1}{9}$

b) $\dfrac{4}{7} - \dfrac{2}{5}$

Think: What do 7 and 9 go into?   Think: What do 7 and 5 go into?

Work out the following Questions, giving the answers in simplest form.

4 $\dfrac{2}{3} + \dfrac{1}{6}$

5 $\dfrac{5}{12} + \dfrac{1}{4}$

6 $\dfrac{1}{4} + \dfrac{3}{8}$

7 $\dfrac{3}{5} + \dfrac{1}{10}$

8 $\dfrac{4}{7} - \dfrac{1}{2}$

9 $\dfrac{3}{5} - \dfrac{1}{4}$

10 $\dfrac{1}{3} + \dfrac{1}{2}$

11 $\dfrac{7}{8} - \dfrac{1}{2}$

12 $\dfrac{2}{5} + \dfrac{1}{3}$

13 $\dfrac{1}{7} + \dfrac{1}{2}$

14 $\dfrac{2}{3} + \dfrac{1}{4}$

15 $\dfrac{1}{5} - \dfrac{1}{6}$

16 $\dfrac{7}{9} - \dfrac{1}{6}$

17 $\dfrac{2}{3} - \dfrac{5}{12}$

18 $\dfrac{7}{10} - \dfrac{1}{3}$

19 $\dfrac{4}{5} - \dfrac{2}{7}$

20 From his weekly money, Frank spends $\dfrac{1}{4}$ on food and $\dfrac{1}{3}$ on rent.

What total fraction of his money does he spend on food and rent?

On these pages you will learn how to write one number as a percentage of another number

7% means 7 out of 100 = $\frac{7}{100}$

If the *denominator* (bottom part of the fraction) is 100, the *numerator* (top of the fraction) tells us the percentage.

$\frac{23}{100}$

Denominator = 100 so numerator shows $\frac{23}{100}$ is 23%

If the denominator is not 100, try and find an *equivalent fraction* where the denominator is 100.

Examples

$\overset{\times\,10}{\frac{2}{10}} = \underset{\times\,10}{\frac{20}{100}} = 20\%$

Denominator now 100

Write 8 as a percentage of 10.
This means 8 out of 10

$= \overset{\times\,10}{\frac{8}{10}} = \underset{\times\,10}{\frac{80}{100}} = 80\%$

Denominator now 100

$\overset{\times\,4}{\frac{2}{25}} = \underset{\times\,4}{\frac{8}{100}} = 8\%$

Denominator now 100

Joel scored 7 out of 20 in a test.
Write this as a percentage.

$\overset{\times\,5}{\frac{7}{20}} = \underset{\times\,5}{\frac{35}{100}} = 35\%$

Denominator now 100

Ⓜ

(1) Write these fractions as percentages:

a) $\frac{27}{100}$ c) $\frac{15}{100}$ e) $\frac{41}{100}$ g) $\frac{91}{100}$ i) $\frac{75}{100}$

b) $\frac{4}{100}$ d) $\frac{21}{100}$ f) $\frac{16}{100}$ h) $\frac{1}{100}$ j) $\frac{12}{100}$

(2) Change the following fractions into percentages:

a) $\frac{5}{10}$ b) $\frac{9}{10}$ c) $\frac{6}{10}$ d) $\frac{3}{10}$ e) $\frac{4}{10}$ f) $\frac{7}{10}$

(3) Use your answers from Question **(2)** to:

a) Write 5 as a percentage of 10   d) Write 3 as a percentage of 10

b) Write 9 as a percentage of 10   e) Write 4 as a percentage of 10

c) Write 6 as a percentage of 10   f) Write 7 as a percentage of 10

(4) Change the following fractions to percentages by multiplying the denominator and numerator of the fractions by 4:

a) $\frac{4}{25}$ b) $\frac{9}{25}$ c) $\frac{15}{25}$ d) $\frac{14}{25}$ e) $\frac{6}{25}$ f) $\frac{7}{25}$

(5) Use your answers from Question **(4)** to:

a) Write 4 as a percentage of 25   d) Write 14 as a percentage of 25

b) Write 9 as a percentage of 25   e) Write 6 as a percentage of 25

c) Write 15 as a percentage of 25   f) Write 7 as a percentage of 25

(6) Some pupils in year 9 did a Maths test marked out of 10. The results are shown below. Change the marks into percentages:

a) $\frac{8}{10}$ b) $\frac{2}{10}$ c) $\frac{1}{10}$ d) $\frac{10}{10}$

(7) In another test, marked out of 20, the results were as follows. Write these marks as percentages:

a) $\frac{6}{20}$ b) $\frac{9}{20}$ c) $\frac{5}{20}$ d) $\frac{11}{20}$ e) $\frac{14}{20}$ f) $\frac{19}{20}$

(8) The table below shows the marks Shamina got in her end of term exams. Copy and complete the table.

SUBJECT	MARK	OUT OF	PERCENTAGE
ART	3	10	
BIOLOGY	13	20	
CHEMISTRY	15	20	
DESIGN	31	50	
FRENCH	16	25	
GERMAN	19	25	
GEOGRAPHY	11	50	
HISTORY	16	20	

Using a calculator to change fractions into percentages

> Divide the numerator by the denominator and multiply by 100.

Examples

$\frac{3}{8}$ = [3] [÷] [8] [×] [1] [0] [0] [=] 37.5%

$\frac{7}{35}$ = [7] [÷] [3] [5] [×] [1] [0] [0] [=] 20%

E

1 Use a calculator to change the fractions below into percentages:

a) $\frac{5}{8}$ e) $\frac{9}{60}$ i) $\frac{28}{35}$ m) $\frac{7}{35}$

b) $\frac{15}{60}$ f) $\frac{16}{40}$ j) $\frac{16}{80}$ n) $\frac{9}{36}$

c) $\frac{26}{80}$ g) $\frac{24}{40}$ k) $\frac{12}{40}$ o) $\frac{7}{28}$

d) $\frac{14}{16}$ h) $\frac{21}{70}$ l) $\frac{18}{90}$

2 Tamsin scored 27 out of 60 in a Science test. What percentage did she score?

3 Seb scored 36 out of 90 in a History exam. What percentage did he score?

4 Louise earns £300 each week. She pays £108 each week to rent her flat. What percentage of her money does she pay in rent each week?

5 The chains in a factory sometimes break.

Out of 400 chains, just 8 chains broke in 2004. What percentage of the chains broke?

6 20 000 people went to a concert. Of these people 4500 were girls. What percentage of the people at the concert were girls?

On these pages you will reduce ratios to their simplest form and use ratios to divide amounts.

Ⓜ Part One

A television programme is shown on three days in every week. Copy and complete the table.

①

Number of weeks	1	2	3	4	5	6	7	8	9	10
Number of programmes	3									

② Make a similar table for a programme which is shown every day of the week.

Copy and complete these sentences for each of the patterns below.

a) For every one red square there is/are ☐ green square(s).

b) 1 in every ☐ squares is red.

③

⑤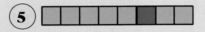

⑦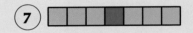

④

⑥

⑧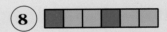

In this diagram 'the RATIO of red squares to green squares is 6:2'.

Both numbers in the ratio 6:2 can be *divided by* 2 so we can REDUCE the ratio 6:2 to its SIMPLEST FORM of 3:1.

Example

The ratio 9:21 is the same as 3:7 (divide by 3).

3:7 is its *SIMPLEST FORM*.

---

⑨ Change the following ratios to their simplest form.

a) 4:2	f) 12:8	k) 10:50	p) 24:18
b) 6:3	g) 15:10	l) 10:25	q) 49:14
c) 10:5	h) 18:12	m) 36:24	r) 81:27
d) 4:8	i) 25:20	n) 10:8	s) 55:22
e) 6:12	j) 30:20	o) 14:21	t) 45:18

Ⓜ **Part Two**

Example

Share a prize of £72 between Angela, Bill and Carl in the ratio 3:1:4.

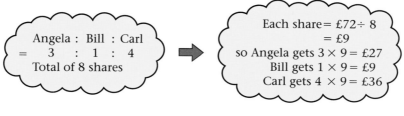

[Check: 27 + 9 + 36 = 72]

1 a) Wayne and Sheila share £350 in the ratio 4:3. How much does Sheila get?

 b) Marika and Leonard share a scratch-card win of £500 in the ratio 3:2. How much is Marika's share?

2 Divide each amount of money below in the ratio given:

 a) £10, 3:2 f) £100, 1:4 k) £200, 2:3:5

 b) £20, 4:1 g) £90, 5:4 l) £240, 1:3:4

 c) £60, 2:1 h) £45, 4:5 m) £900, 1:3:5

 d) £25, 2:3 i) £120, 7:5 n) £600, 3:4:5

 e) £80, 3:5 j) £56, 5:3 o) £1100, 2:4:5

3 Jason and Margaret share a ski-lift bill of £56 in the ratio 5:3. How much does Jason pay?

4 A sum of money was shared in the ratio 7:2. If the smaller share was £10, how much was the larger share? What was the sum of money shared out?

5 The ratio of pupils with fair hair to those with dark hair in year 9 is 3:7. If there are 14 pupils with dark hair, how many pupils have fair hair?

6 In a box of mixed biscuits the ratio of chocolate biscuits to plain ones is 2:7. There are 12 chocolate biscuits in the box. How many plain ones are there?

Note

Before reducing a ratio to its simplest form, make sure the *units are the same* for all the numbers.

Example

The ratio 2 km:300 m is the same as 2000 m:300 m.
2000:300 reduces to 20:3 (divide by 100)
The *simplest form* of 2 km:300 m is 20:3.

2 m:50 cm is the same as 200 cm:50 cm, which is the same as 4:1.

same units

E

1 Change the following ratios to their simplest form.

a) 1 m : 50 cm   d) 100 g : 1 kg   g) 250 m : 2 km

b) 1 m : 25 cm   e) 200 g : 1 kg   h) 300 ml : 1 l

c) 50 cm : 2 m   f) 2 kg : 500 g   i) 3 kg : 600 g

2 Reduce 80 mm:16 cm:24 cm to its simplest form.

3 Reduce 500 cm:10 m:30 m to its simplest form.

4 Reduce 100 g:500 g:1 kg to its simplest form.

5 In February (28 days), the ratio of wet days to dry days was 3:4. How many wet days were there?

6 In a box of 270 biro pens, the ratio of blue to red to black was 2:3:4. How many black biros were there?

7 A pet shop sells hamsters, mice and donkeys in the ratio 7:5:2.

If it sells 35 mice, how many donkeys does it sell?

8 At a rock concert, the ratio of boys:girls:adults was 60:50:5. If there were 20 adults, how many boys were there?

On this page you will find the value of one item to help you find the value of several items.

Example

If 7 T-shirts cost £56, how much will 10 T-shirts cost?

> Find the cost of one T-shirt

1 T-shirt costs £56 ÷ 7 = £8

so 10 T-shirts cost £8 × 10 = £80

M

1. 5 doughnuts cost 80p. How much will 12 doughnuts cost?

2. 8 m² of cloth cost £24. How much will 5 m² cost?

3. Alain paid £18 for 6 tropical fish. How much would he pay for 10 tropical fish?

4. Sergio bought 3 CD's as presents. He paid £27 for them. How much would 7 CD's cost?

5. The school shop sells 6 coloured pencils for 48p. How much would 15 coloured pencils cost?

6. A go-cart can do 24 laps of the track on 3 litres of petrol. How many laps could it do on 10 litres?

7. Biros cost 96 pence per dozen (12). How much would 5 biros cost?

8. 30 envelopes cost 90 pence. How much would 50 envelopes cost?

E

1. 6 adults can go to the cinema for £9.60. How much would 10 adults pay?

2. 7 cans of cola cost £2.10. How much would 12 cans cost?

3. 9 litres of cooking oil cost £4.50. How much would 15 litres of cooking oil cost?

4. 15 kg of potatoes cost £3.00. How much does 8 kg cost?

5. In 8 days a builder lays 24 000 bricks. How many days will it take him to lay 60 000 bricks?

6. A recipe for a pizza, which serves five people, contains 150 grams of flour, 100 grams of cheese, 20 grams of garlic sausage and 150 ml of water. If you wanted to make the pizza for 8 people, how much would you need of

   a) flour   b) cheese   c) water?

On these pages you will use percentages to increase and decrease numbers.

Remember

        'increase' means 'make bigger'   'reduce' means 'make smaller'

                'decrease' means 'make smaller'

Example

(a) | Decrease | £90 by 20%.

    FIND PERCENTAGE FIRST

    10% of 90 = 90 ÷ 10 = 9

    so 20% of 90 = 18

    | Decrease | £90 by £18

    Answer = 90 | − | 18

           = £72

(b) | Increase | £17 by 10%,

    FIND PERCENTAGE FIRST.

    10% of 17 = 1.7

    We say £1.70

    | Increase | £17 by £1.70

    Answer = 17 | + | 1.70

           = £18.70

Ⓜ

① Work out

a) 10% of £80   f) 20% of 150 cm   k) 25% of 32

b) 10% of £60   g) 20% of 90 cm   l) 25% of 640

c) 10% of £120   h) 20% of 50 grams   m) 25% of 44

d) 10% of £350   i) 20% of 750 miles   n) 25% of 1600

e) 10% of £480   j) 20% of 70 kg   o) 25% of 96

② Copy and fill in the empty boxes below:

a) £35   10% = ☐   20% = ☐

b) £28   10% = ☐   20% = ☐

c) £63   10% = ☐   30% = ☐

d) £87   10% = ☐   60% = ☐

e) £112   10% = ☐   20% = ☐

f) £15   10% = ☐   40% = ☐

③ Copy and complete the table.

£350	10% =	Increase £350 by 10% (+) =
£420	10% =	Increase £420 by 10% (+) =
£150	20% =	Decrease £150 by 20% (−) =
£60	20% =	Increase £60 by 20% (+) =
£88	25% =	Decrease £88 by 25% (−) =
£20	50% =	Increase £20 by 50% (+) =

④ Copy and fill in the empty boxes below:

(a) £460   10% = ☐   5% = ☐   15% = ☐

Increase £460 by 15% = 460 + ☐ = £ ☐

(b) £180   10% = ☐   5% = ☐   15% = ☐

Decrease £180 by 15% = 180 − ☐ = £ ☐

(c) £120   10% = ☐   30% = ☐

Increase £120 by 30% = ☐ + ☐ = £ ☐

(d) £2600   1% = ☐   3% = ☐

Increase £2600 by 3% = ☐ + ☐ = £ ☐

(e) £800   1% = ☐   4% = ☐   10% = ☐   14% = ☐

Reduce £800 by 14% = ☐ − ☐ = £ ☐

(f) £1200 1% = ☐   6% = ☐   10% = ☐   16% = ☐

Decrease £1200 by 16% = ☐ − ☐ = £ ☐

⑤ (a) Decrease £76 by 10%.

(b) Reduce £82 by 10%.

(c) A light bulb normally costs £3.
Reduce the price by 20%

For each of the following items in a sale, find:

(a) the amount the price is reduced.

(b) the new price.

6
PERSONAL STEREO
£15
10% off

7
CD PLAYER
£13
10% off

8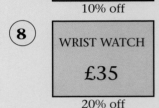
WRIST WATCH
£35
20% off

9
BODY RING
£15
20% off

10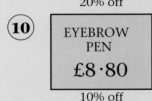
EYEBROW PEN
£8·80
10% off

11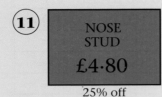
NOSE STUD
£4·80
25% off

12
SLAVE BANGLE
£55
20% off

13
BIG-MAC
£1.20
25% off

14
PENDANTS
£24
25% off

15
JEWELLERY BOX
£34
20% off

16
BRACELET WATCH
£98
10% off

17
ALARM CLOCK
£5·20
25% off

18
PHOTO FRAME
£12·50
20% off

19
COSMETIC SET
£18
15% off

20
MANICURE SET
£12·80
25% off

Percentage problems can be worked out *with a calculator*.

Examples

(a) Find 7% of £48.

FIND 1% ➡ ÷ 100

THEN 7% ➡ × 7

Answer:

48 ÷ 100 × 7 = £3.36.

(b) Increase £206 by 12%.

FIND PERCENTAGE FIRST.

206 ÷ 100 × 12 = £24.72

Increase £206 by £24.72

Answer = 206 + 24.72.

= £230.72.

E

Use a calculator to answer the following questions:

1 a) Find 3% of £70   b) Increase £70 by 3%

2 a) Find 6% of £55   b) Increase £55 by 6%

3 a) Find 7% of £92   b) Decrease £92 by 7%

4 a) Find 9% of £562   b) Decrease £562 by 9%

5 a) Find 3% of £742   b) Increase £742 by 3%

6 Increase £126 by 17%   **9** Increase £7400 by 3%

7 Reduce £1950 by 11%   **10** Increase £6280 by 9%

8 Decrease £469 by 5%   **11** Decrease £5960 by 3%

12 A used-car salesman cuts prices by the percentages shown in the table.
Copy and complete the table to show the new prices.

Car	Price (£)	% cut	Actual cut (in £)	New price (£)
Vauxhall Astra	3200	3%		
Rover 75	8400	7%		
Ford Mondeo	1800	4%		
Honda Civic	3900	10%		
Volvo Estate	6500	8%		

13 Luigi earns £17050 each year. He is given a 5% pay *rise*. How much does he now earn each year?

14 Lisa earns £31600 each year. She is given a 3% pay *rise*. How much does she now earn each year?

15 At the World Cup rugby match, there were 76500 people. 12% of these people had a flag painted on their faces. How many people did *not* have a flag painted on their faces?

16 Mo buys an armchair for £500. She must pay an extra 17.5% (called VAT – Value Added Tax). How much money in total must Mo pay for the armchair?

17 In the very hot summer of 2010, wine production went down by 17%. If 500000 bottles are *usually* made, how many bottles were made in 2010?

Decimals, Fractions and Percentages

On these pages you will compare decimals, fractions and percentages.

Remember:

$\frac{1}{10} = 0.1$ $\frac{1}{100} = 0.01$ $\frac{2}{1000} = 0.002$

$1\% = \frac{1}{100}$ $76\% = \frac{76}{100}$ $\frac{3}{10} = \frac{3}{100} = 30\%$

Write True or False for each of the following statements.

1 $\frac{82}{100} = 0.08$ **7** $\frac{94}{100} = 0.94$ **13** $0.521 = \frac{521}{1000}$

2 $\frac{7}{10} = 0.07$ **8** $\frac{1}{2} = 0.2$ **14** $0.23 = \frac{23}{1000}$

3 $\frac{1}{4} = 0.25$ **9** $0.001 = \frac{1}{1000}$ **15** $0.75 = \frac{3}{4}$

4 $\frac{1}{100} = 0.01$ **10** $0.003 = \frac{3}{100}$ **16** $0.6 = \frac{6}{10}$

5 $\frac{3}{4} = 0.34$ **11** $0.2 = \frac{1}{2}$

6 $\frac{1}{10} = 0.1$ **12** $0.09 = \frac{9}{100}$

17 Match each of these fractions with one of these decimals.

$\frac{2}{10}$	0.5
$\frac{5}{100}$	0.75
$\frac{1}{2}$	0.05
$\frac{3}{10}$	0.3
$\frac{3}{4}$	0.55
$\frac{55}{100}$	0.2

Write as fractions.

18 8%   **21** 77%   **24** 0.37

19 11%   **22** 0.7   **25** 6%

20 29%   **23** 0.03   **26** 0.187

Write as percentages.

27 0.16   **30** 0.4   **33** $\frac{1}{2}$

28 0.29   **31** $\frac{21}{100}$ **34** 0.71

29 0.04   **32** $\frac{39}{100}$ **35** $\frac{5}{100}$

In Questions **36** to **41** write down which is the larger amount.

36 (0.2 $\frac{1}{2}$)   **38** (20%   0.3)   **40** (12% $\frac{9}{100}$)

37 (6%   0.6)   **39** ($\frac{7}{100}$ 5%)   **41** ($\frac{4}{10}$ 30%)

Examples.

4.31 is the same as $4\frac{31}{100}$

6.3 is the same as $6\frac{3}{10}$

$2\frac{7}{10} = 2.7$ $5\frac{39}{100} = 5.39$

E

Write as fractions.

(1) 2.72   **(3)** 7.75   **(5)** 1.05   **(7)** 3.9

(2) 0.692   **(4)** 3.427   **(6)** 6.081   **(8)** 5.006

Write as decimals.

(9) £$2\frac{63}{100}$ **(11)** £$7\frac{1}{4}$ **(13)** $4\frac{129}{1000}$ km   **(15)** $6\frac{3}{10}$ cm

(10) £$5\frac{9}{10}$ **(12)** £$9\frac{7}{100}$ **(14)** $2\frac{3}{4}$ km   **(16)** $1\frac{38}{1000}$ km

Give the answer as a decimal.

(17) $0.38 + \frac{1}{4}$ **(19)** $\frac{3}{5} + 0.2$ **(21)** $0.6 + \frac{23}{100}$

(18) $\frac{1}{2} - 0.24$ **(20)** $0.73 - \frac{4}{10}$ **(22)** $\frac{3}{4} - 0.6$

(23) Write a decimal in the box. '$2\frac{3}{5}$ kg of sugar is ☐ kg.'

Give the answer as a percentage.

(24) $21\% + \frac{31}{100}$ **(26)** $\frac{1}{2} - 17\%$ **(28)** $0.7 - 31\%$

(25) $\frac{7}{100} + 64\%$ **(27)** $0.04 + 12\%$ **(29)** $52\% - \frac{1}{4}$

(30) Match each of these fractions with one of these decimals.

$6\frac{3}{100}$	5.85
$1\frac{1}{4}$	8.54
$5\frac{85}{100}$	1.25
$8\frac{54}{100}$	3.001
$3\frac{1}{1000}$	6.03

(31) A full box of cereal contains $\frac{43}{100}$ kg.

At breakfast 0.15 kg is used. How much cereal is left in the box?

In Questions **(32)** to **(34)**, write the numbers in order, starting with the smallest.

(32) $\frac{1}{4}$ 0.21 0.3   **(33)** 0.408 $\frac{48}{100}$ 0.084   **(34)** 0.85 $\frac{3}{4}$ 0.8

On these pages you will tackle number problems using decimals, fractions, percentages, squares, cubes and square roots.

Remember

$40 \times 100 = 4000$

$2.8 \times 100 = 280$ (2.80)

$30 \times 40 = 1200$ $(3 \times 10 \times 4 \times 10 = 12 \times 100)$

$800 \div 20 = 40$ $(8 \times 100) \div (2 \times 10) = (4 \times 10)$

$30 \div 1000 = 0.03$ $(030.)$

M

Copy and complete the squares:

1

×	20	30	60
10	200		
30			
40			

2

×	30	200	500
9			
50			25000
60			

3

×	6	40	90
60			
300			
800			

Work out

4 70×10

5 40×1000

6 3.6×10

7 0.029×100

8 5.2×100

9 66.1×100

10 0.832×10

11 $20 \div 100$

12 $31.8 \div 10$

13 $0.03 \div 100$

14 $0.187 \div 100$

15 $42.9 \div 1000$

Copy and fill in the empty boxes.

16 $900 \div 30 \rightarrow \boxed{} \div 10 \rightarrow \boxed{}$

17 $600 \div 30 \rightarrow \boxed{} \div 10 \rightarrow \boxed{}$

18 $12\,000 \div 40 \rightarrow \boxed{} \div 10 \rightarrow \boxed{}$

19 $24\,000 \div 30 \rightarrow \boxed{} \div 10 \rightarrow \boxed{}$

20 40 people each pay £30 to see a concert. What is the total amount of money they pay?

21 3600 tins of dog food are packed into 90 boxes. How many tins are in each box?

Copy and complete the Questions below by writing the missing number in the box.

(22) $30 \times \boxed{} = 1500$

(23) $50 \times \boxed{} = 1000$

(24) $60 \times \boxed{} = 4200$

(25) $\boxed{} \times 40 = 3200$

(26) $500 \times \boxed{} = 25000$

(27) $600 \div \boxed{} = 20$

(28) $1800 \div \boxed{} = 90$

(29) $2800 \div \boxed{} = 4$

(30) $0.6 \times \boxed{} = 60$

(31) $0.85 \div \boxed{} = 0.085$

(32) $31.6 \div \boxed{} = 0.316$

(33) $\boxed{} \div 100 = 2.874$

Remember

Square of $6 = 6^2 = 6 \times 6 = 36$

Cube of $6 = 6^3 = 6 \times 6 \times 6 = 36 \times 6 = 216$

Square root of $36 = \sqrt{36} = 6$ (because $6 \times 6 = 36$)

E

1. Match the six Questions to the six given answers:

$3^2 + 7$	25
$(3 + 2)^2$	18
$6^2 - 10$	32
$\sqrt{(14 + 2)}$	16
$9 + \sqrt{81}$	4
$5^2 + \sqrt{49}$	26

2. Pam has £36. She spends two-thirds of her money. How much money has she got left?

3. Write $\frac{3}{4}$ as a percentage.

4. What is the cost of 2 CD's at £6.99 each?

5. Which is the larger?

   $\boxed{1\% \text{ of } 376}$ or $\boxed{2\% \text{ of } 182}$

6. The area of a square is 49cm². How long is each side?

7. Increase £600 by 1%.

8. Work out $2 + 3^2 + 2^3$.

9.

	£20	£50	£65
10%	£2	£5	£6.50
5%	£1	£2.50	£3.25

Use the table above to work out the missing numbers in the Questions below:

a) 15% of £50 = £ $\boxed{}$

b) 2.5% of £50 = £ $\boxed{}$

c) £3 = 15% of £ $\boxed{}$

d) £9.75 = 15% of £ $\boxed{}$

10. If $\sqrt{16} = 4$, work out $\sqrt{1600}$.

11. Work out

   $\sqrt{64}$ 3^2 $\sqrt{(28 + 8)}$ $9^2 - 71$

   Which answer is the largest?

On these pages you will round off numbers to the nearest 10, 100 or 1000. You will also round off to the nearest whole number and to 1 decimal place.

Here are cuttings from two newspapers:

A. '1074 bus shelters were vandalised last year at a total cost of £517,638.'

B. '1000 bus shelters were vandalised at a cost of over £500,000.'

In B the figures have been *rounded off* because the reporter thinks that his readers will not be interested in the exact numbers in the report.

Rules for rounding

• Rounding to the nearest whole number.

If the first digit after the decimal point is *5 or more* round *up*.

Otherwise round down.

57.3 → 57

89.8 → 90

5.5 → 6

• Rounding to the nearest 100.

If the digit in the tens column is 5 or more round up.

Otherwise round down.

593 → 600

247 → 200

2643 → 2600

• Rounding to the nearest 10.

If the digit in the units column is 5 or more round up.

Otherwise round down.

27 → 30

42 → 40

265 → 270

• Rounding to the nearest 1000.

If the digit in the hundreds column is 5 or more round up.

Otherwise round down.

1394 → 1000

502 → 1000

11764 → 12000

Ⓜ

(**1**) Round off these numbers to the nearest 10.

a) 73   c) 24   e) 56   g) 242   i) 29   k) 37

b) 58   d) 99   f) 127   h) 18   j) 589   l) 51

(**2**) Round off these numbers to the nearest 100.

a) 584   c) 607   e) 285   g) 222

b) 293   d) 914   f) 655   h) 1486

3 Round off these numbers to the nearest 1000.

    a) 4555   c) 850   e) 614   g) 25712

    b) 757   d) 2251   f) 2874   h) 13568

4 Work out these answers on a calculator and then round off the answer to the *nearest whole number*.

    a) $235 \div 17$ d) $999 \div 17$ g) 53.2×2.3 j) $109 \div 0.7$

    b) $4714 \div 58$ e) 5.62×7.04 h) 12.6×0.93 k) $63.4 \div 11$

    c) $2375 \div 11$ f) 19.3×1.19 i) $119.6 \div 5.1$ l) $1.92 \div 0.09$

5 How long is this rod to:

    a) the nearest cm   b) the nearest 10 cm   c) the nearest metre?

Decimal places

- Using a calculator to work out $25 \div 9$, the answer is 2.777777.

  On a number line we can see that the answer is nearer to 2.8 than to 2.7. We will *round off* the answer to 2.8 correct to 1 *decimal place*.

  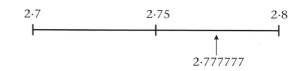

- Using a calculator to work out 11% of 21.23, the answer is 2.3353.

  On a number line we can see that the answer is nearer to 2.3 than to 2.4. So the answer is 2.3, correct to 1 decimal place (1 d.p. for short).

  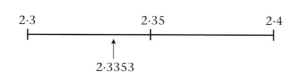

- Suppose the calculator shows 1.75. This number is exactly half way between 1.7 and 1.8. Do we round up or not? The rule for rounding off to 1 decimal place is:

  > If the figure in the 2nd decimal place is 5 or more, round up. Otherwise do not.

Examples: 3.75**3**8 = 3.8 to 1 d.p.

            14.2**8**7 = 14.3 to 1 d.p.

            17.9**5**82 = 18.0 to 1 d.p. (We need the zero!)

- 7.96 rounded to the nearest whole number is 8

  7.96 rounded to 1 decimal place is 8.0. [The zero is needed.]

E

1 Round these numbers to 1 decimal place.

a) 2.41   b) 8.94   c) 4.65   d) 12.47

2 Round these numbers to 1 decimal place.

a) 1.924   b) 4.065   c) 9.997   d) 65.374

3 Write the following numbers correct to 1 decimal place.

a) 18.7864   c) 17.0946   e) 5.421   g) 10.252
b) 3.55   d) 0.7624   f) 11.27   h) 7.084

4 Write the following numbers correct to the nearest whole number.

a) 3.75821   c) 0.38214   e) 11.444   g) 6.5781
b) 11.64412   d) 138.2972   f) 7.058   h) 5.3092

5 Round each number:

a) to the nearest whole number,
b) to one decimal place

   i) 8.41   ii) 0.782   iii) 7.92   iv) 4.95

6 Work out the following on a calculator and write the answer correct to 1 decimal place.

a) $11 \div 7$ c) $1.4 \div 6$ e) 1.3×0.95 g) $97 \div 1.3$
b) $213 \div 11$ d) $29 \div 13$ f) 1.23×3.71 h) 0.95×8.3

7 Measure the lines below and give the lengths in cm correct to one decimal place

a) _____

b) _____

c) _____

d) _____

e) _____

8 Measure the dimensions of the rectangles below.

a) Write down the length and width in cm, correct to one decimal place.
b) Work out the area of each rectangle and give the answer in cm², correct to one decimal place.

i)   ii)

Collecting like terms and brackets 1

On these pages you will collect like terms and multiply out brackets.

Examples

1 $2a + 5b + 2b + 3a$
$= 5a + 7b$

2 $6a + 2b - a$
$= 5a + 2b$

3 *Remember $2a + 5$ is not $7a$*
$2a + 5$ cannot be simplified.

M

Collect like terms

1 $7a + 3b + 2a$

2 $5a + 6b + 2b$

3 $9a + 3a + 7b$

4 $6c - c + 3d$

5 $4c + 7d - 3d$

6 $8c - 2c + 3d - d$

7 $6x + 3y + 5y - 2y$

8 $5p + 9p - 3p + 2q$

9 $10p - 4p + 6q - 4q$

10 $5p + 7 + 2q - q$

11 $8x + 3x + 9 - 2$

12 $2x + 1 + 8 - x$

13 $5p + 3p + 6 - p + 7$

14 $5x + 3y - 2x + 4$

15 $15a + 10 + 3 + 4a$

Find the perimeter of the following shapes:

16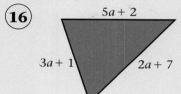

17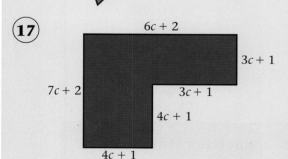

18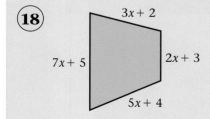

19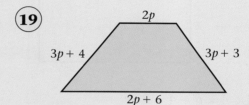

20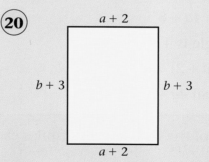

21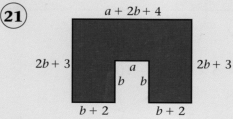

Collect like terms in Questions **22** to **25**.

22 $7a + 3a + 5b + 9b + 6a + 8b$

23 $6p + 9q - 3p + 8q - 2p - 3q$

24 $8x + 8 + 7x - 3 + 2y - 3x$

25 $9p + 6p + 12q - 5p + 9 + 4q$

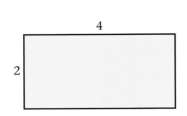

4

2

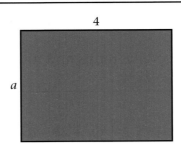

4

a

Area of rectangle = 4 × 2 = 8

Area of rectangle = 4 × *a* = 4*a*

Put these two rectangles together to make a large rectangle

4

a

(*a* + 2)

2

4

Total area must be 4 × *a* + 4 × 2

$$= 4a + 8$$

Total area of rectangle is 4 × (*a* + 2)

This is written as 4(*a* + 2)

so 4(*a* + 2) must equal 4*a* + 8

A number in front of the brackets, multiplies each of the numbers or symbols inside the brackets.

Examples

$5(a + 2) = 5 \times a + 5 \times 2 = 5a + 10$

$6(x + 3) = 6x + 18$

$3(x - 2) = 3x - 6$

$4(2x + 1) = 8x + 4$

$2(1 + 3x) = 2 + 6x$

In Questions **1** to **15** remove the brackets.

1 $3(x + 4)$

2 $5(x + 3)$

3 $4(x - 2)$

4 $6(x - 2)$

5 $2(2x + 1)$

6 $3(2x + 3)$

7 $4(3x + 1)$

8 $3(4x + 5)$

9 $9(2 - x)$

10 $2(4x - 5)$

11 $7(3x - 1)$

12 $10(2x + 5)$

13 $5(3x - 5)$

14 $2(3 - 2x)$

15 $3(x + y)$

In Questions **16** to **21**, find the area of each rectangle. Remove the brackets in your answers.

16
6
$(a + 3)$

17
5
$(2a + 1)$

18
3
$(4a - 2)$

19
8
$(2x + 3)$

20
$(5x - 2)$
2

21
$(3a + 5)$
6

22 a) Find the area of the picture.

b) Find the perimeter of the picture.

5

$x + 3$

On these pages you will write equations and solve equations.

Solve $5n + 2 = 32$

$\boxed{5n} + 2 = 32$

$5n = 30$

$n = 6$

because $5 \times \boxed{6} = 30$

Solve $4n - 6 = 6$

$\boxed{4n} - 6 = 6$

$4n = 12$

$n = 3$

because $4 \times \boxed{3} = 12$

Solve the following equations:

(1) $n + 3 = 12$

(2) $n + 7 = 11$

(3) $n + 8 = 13$

(4) $n + 12 = 20$

(5) $n - 6 = 4$

(6) $n - 3 = 7$

(7) $n - 8 = 12$

(8) $n - 2 = 2$

(9) $8 = n - 6$

(10) $12 = n - 4$

(11) $0 = n - 2$

(12) $3 = n + 2$

Solve the following equations:

(13) $2n + 1 = 7$

(14) $3n - 2 = 13$

(15) $4n - 6 = 14$

(16) $3n + 11 = 20$

(17) $12 = 2n + 4$

(18) $16 = 3n - 5$

(19) $21 = 14 + n$

(20) $0 = 2n - 10$

(21) $3n - 4 = 17$

(22) $6n + 2 = 26$

(23) $5n - 17 = 18$

(24) $3n - 6 = 6$

In each Question below, I am thinking of a number. Write down an equation then solve it to find the number.

(1) If we multiply the number by 2 then add 1, the answer is 5 (so $2n + 1 = 5$ then solve).

(2) If we multiply the number by 4 then subtract 2, the answer is 6.

(3) If we multiply the number by 3 then add 4, the answer is 16.

(4) If we double the number then add 6, the answer is 14.

(5) If we multiply the number by 5 then subtract 4, the answer is 21.

(6) If we multiply the number by 6 then subtract 2, the answer is 10.

(7) If we multiply the number by 7 then add 5, the answer is 26.

(8) If we multiply the number by 10 then add 6, the answer is 56.

Here are cross number puzzles with a difference. There are no clues, only answers, and you have to find where the answers go.

a) Copy out the cross number pattern.

b) Fit all the given numbers into the correct spaces. Work logically and tick off the numbers from lists as you write them in the squares.

1

2 digits	3 digits	4 digits	5 digits
18	122	3845	36352
25	128	7810	36742
33	310		51362
34	561		
53	624		
66	773		

2

2 digits	3 digits	4 digits	5 digits
17	271	1842	32675
34	351	3081	41795
42	698	4825	43875
60	802	4864	48364
64	805	5067	66274
73	813	5267	
80	858	9344	
91			

3

2 digits	3 digits	4 digits	5 digits	7 digits
28	254	1783	26414	5381074
31	255	2837	37832	
51	256	2892	42207	
52	313	3167	47932	
61	402	4624	49362	
72	449	9237		
94	637			
	646			

4

2 digits	3 digits	4 digits	5 digits
13	174	1276	18131
14	505	1563	18682
28	543	2317	32561
38	617	4513	38473
38	845	5347	41861
49	874	6347	42561
81		6527	45555
86		6887	58182
		7575	58761
		8192	82831
		8437	83147

6 digits	7 digits
525143	5261458
738589	
825589	

5 This one is more difficult.

2 digits	3 digits	4 digits	5 digits
15	106	2623	21562
18	289	2634	22919
24	399	3215	22961
28	499	4211	28557
36	683	4215	46963
86	835	5285	47993
92		6218	52963
98		7362	53999
		8116	83014
		8348	83562
		8718	94241

6 digits	7 digits
235627	3245802
627622	
825627	

Parallel and Perpendicular Lines

On these pages you will explore lines.

Parallel lines are lines that are the same distance apart for all their length. Railway lines are parallel lines.

Perpendicular lines cross or meet at right angles.

Two lines that cross each other are called intersecting lines. The point at which they cross is an intersection.

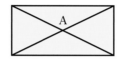

Point A is the intersection of the diagonals of the rectangle.

---

1 This trapezium has two parallel sides. Copy the shape and put arrows on the two parallel sides.

2 This diagram has two perpendicular lines. Copy the shape. Show the perpendicular lines by marking right angles (like the example at the top of the page).

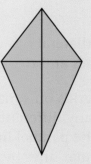

3 This is a football pitch. Use squared paper. Copy this football pitch (do not do the circles if they are too tricky).
Show all the parallel lines with arrows or coloured pens or pencils, using a different colour for each pair of parallel lines. Show all the perpendicular lines by marking right angles.

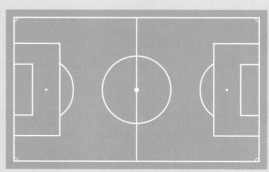

4

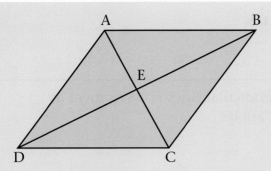

Here is a rhombus with its diagonals

Copy and complete the following. Put in the word 'parallel' or 'perpendicular'.

(a) AD is... to BC

(b) DC is .... to AB

(c) AE is .... to EB

(d) BA is... to CD

(e) EC is .... to DE

E

1 Copy the diagram.

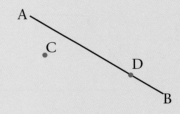

(a) Draw a line through C which is perpendicular to AB.

(b) Draw a line through D which is perpendicular to AB.

(c) Draw a line through C which is parallel to AB.

2 This quadrilateral has one pair of
parallel lines and two pairs of perpendicular lines.

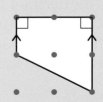

Use 3 × 3 grids on squared or dotty paper.
Find as many different quadrilaterals as you can.
Show all the parallel lines with arrows and show all the
perpendicular lines by marking a right angle.

3 Draw round a regular hexagon template (or trace the diagram).
Draw on all the diagonals. How many intersections are there?

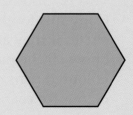

4 Investigate the diagonals of irregular hexagons.
Do you get the same result?

('irregular' means 'all the sides are *not* equal')

On these pages you will calculate angles on a straight line, at a point and in a triangle.
You will also use vertically opposite angles.

Reminder

- ANGLES ON A STRAIGHT LINE
  The angles on a straight line add up to 180°.
  $x + 33° = 180°$
  $x = 147°$

- ANGLES AT A POINT
  The angles at a point add up to 360°.

  100°
  150°   110°

- ANGLES IN A TRIANGLE
  The angles in a triangle add up to 180°.
  $y + 60° + 40° = 180°$
  $y + 100° = 180°$
  $y = 80°$

  y
  60°   40°

- VERTICALLY OPPOSITE ANGLES
  When two lines intersect, the opposite angles are equal.

  z
  48°

  $z = 48°$
  The angles 48° and z are vertically opposite.

Ⓜ

Find the angles marked with the letters.

1 a 35°

2 145° b

3 38° c

4 42° d 42°

5 45° e

6 f 110° 130°

7 100° 170° g

8 30° h

9 55° i

10 j 70°

11 40° m k l

12 106° p n o

13 80° 70° q

14 53° r 77°

15 s 30° 125°

16 105° 115° 65° t

E

Find the angles marked with the letters.

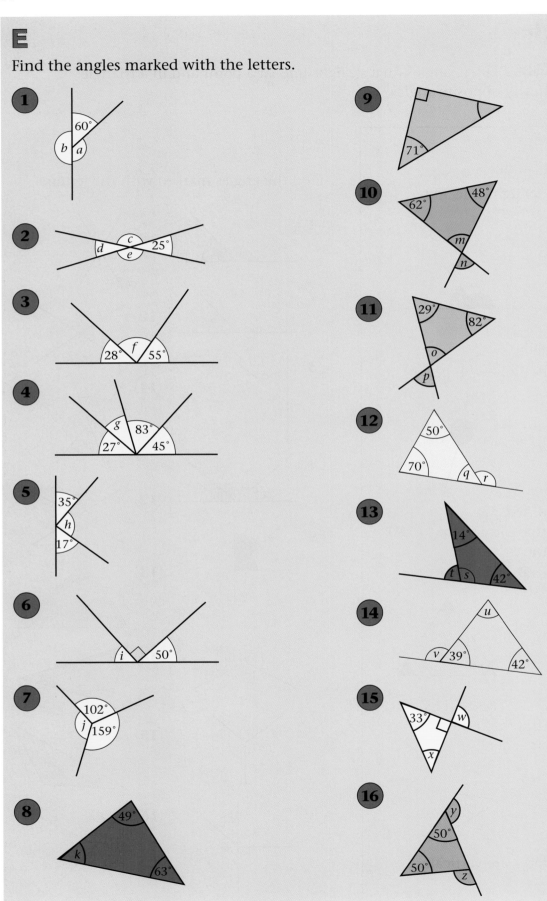

1 60°, b, a

2 c, 25°, d, e

3 28°, f, 55°

4 g, 83°, 27°, 45°

5 35°, h, 17°

6 i, 50°

7 102°, j, 159°

8 49°, k, 63°

9 71°

10 62°, 48°, m, n

11 29°, 82°, o, p

12 50°, 70°, q, r

13 14°, t, s, 42°

14 u, v, 39°, 42°

15 33°, w, x

16 y, 50°, 50°, z

On these pages you will use alternate and corresponding angles.

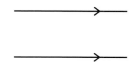

These arrows show
that the 2 lines
are parallel

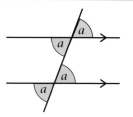

All the acute angles
marked *a* are equal

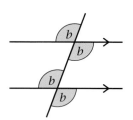

All the obtuse angles
marked *b* are equal

Many people think of
'Z' angles (*alternate* angles) and 'F' angles (*corresponding* angles)

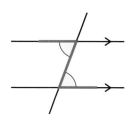

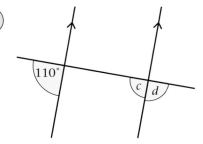

Alternate angles are equal

Corresponding angles are equal

Examples

Find the angles marked with letters.

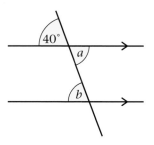

$a = 40°$
$b = 40°$

$c = 110°$
$d = 70°$

M

Find the angles marked with the letters.

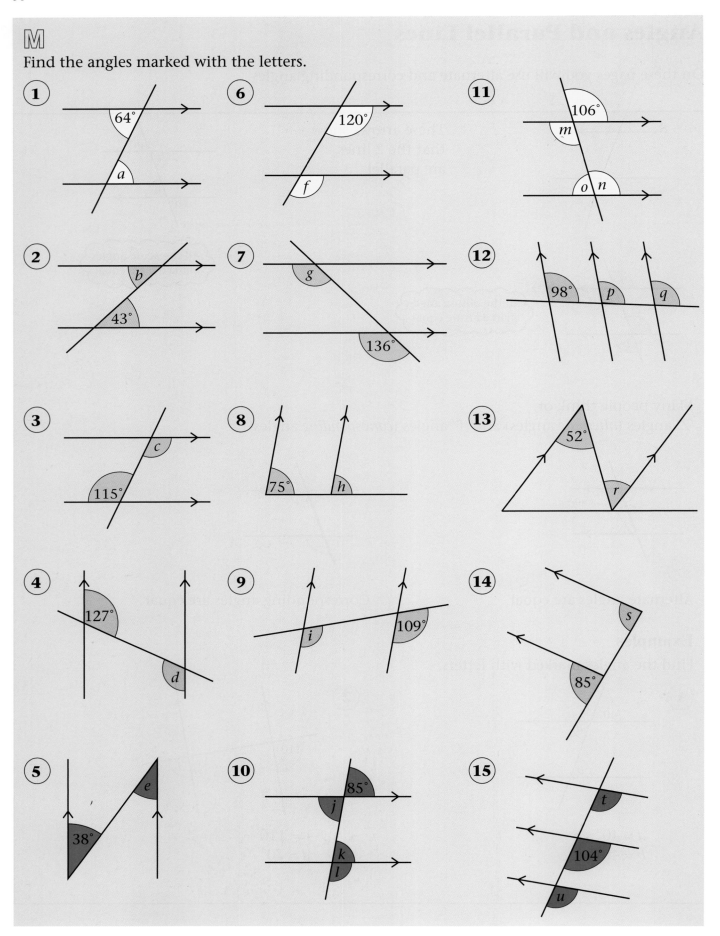

1 64° a

2 b 43°

3 c 115°

4 127° d

5 e 38°

6 120° f

7 g 136°

8 75° h

9 i 109°

10 85° j k l

11 106° m o n

12 98° p q

13 52° r

14 s 85°

15 t 104° u

Example

Find the angles marked with letters.

$a = 65°$

$b = 115°$

$c = 87°$

$d = 93°$

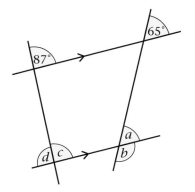

E

1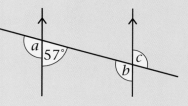

2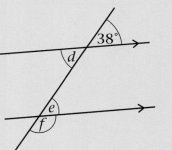

3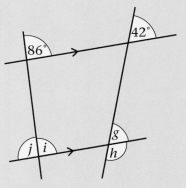

4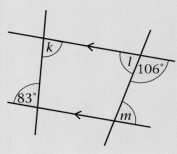

5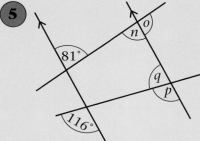

6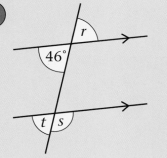

7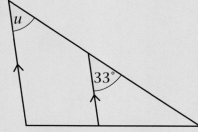

8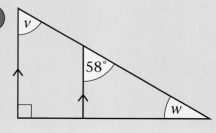

Reminder

A quadrilateral is a shape with 4 straight sides.

Angles in quadrilaterals

Draw a quadrilateral of any shape on a piece of paper or card and cut it out. Mark the four angles *a*, *b*, *c*, and *d* and tear them off.

Arrange the four angles about a point

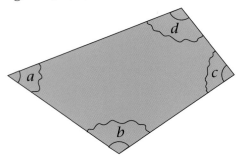

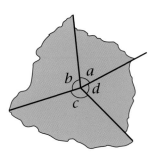

The angles in the quadrilateral add up to 360°

Ⓜ

Find the angles marked with the letters.

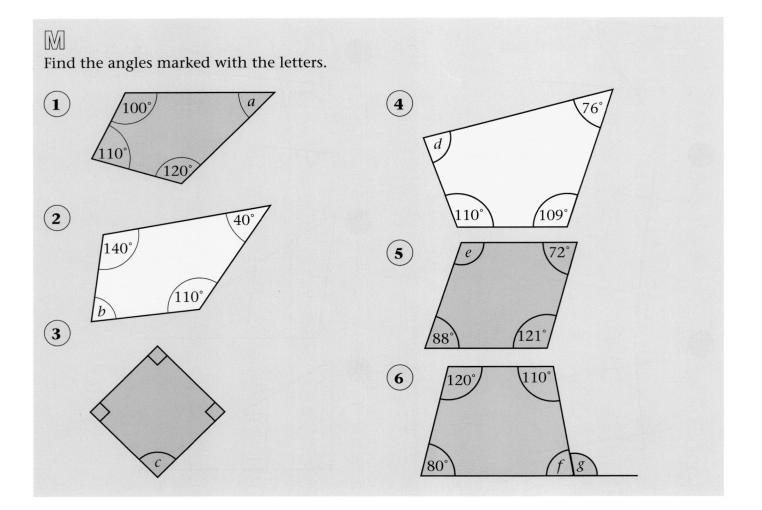

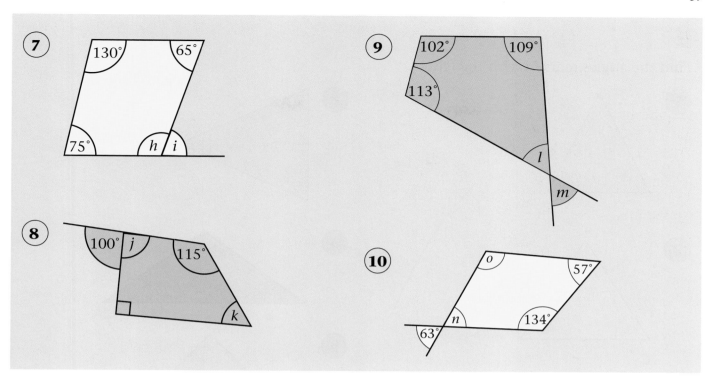

(7) 130° 65° 75° *h* *i*

(9) 102° 109° 113° *l* *m*

(8) 100° *j* 115° *k*

(10) *o* 57° *n* 134° 63°

Special Triangles

An *isosceles* triangle has
2 equal sides and 2 equal angles.

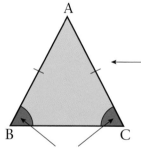

The sides AB and AC are marked with a 'dash' which means that these sides are equal.

Angles B and C are equal.

An *equilateral* triangle has
3 equal sides and 3 equal angles (all 60°).

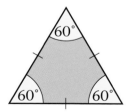

Examples

Find the angles marked with the letters.

(1)

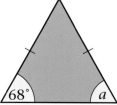

68° *a*

a = 68° (isosceles triangle)

(2)

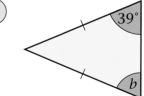

39° *b*

b = 39° (isosceles triangle)

E

Find the angles marked with the letters.

1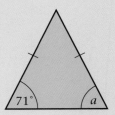
71°   *a*

2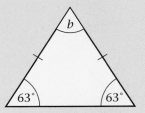
b   63°   63°

3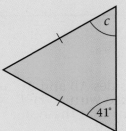
c   41°

4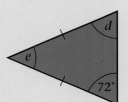
d   *e*   72°

5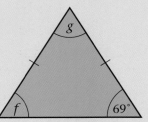
g   *f*   69°

6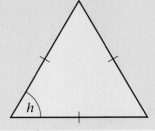
h

7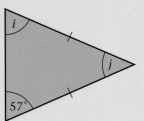
i   *j*   57°

8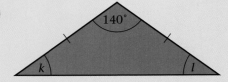
140°   *k*   *l*

9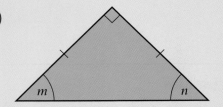
m   *n*

10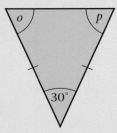
o   *p*   30°

11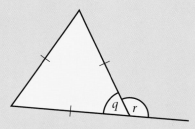
q   *r*

12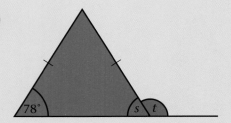
78°   *s*   *t*

Go for a Swim

The cost and opening times of Rabdale swimming pool are shown below.

	cost per session
adult	£3.85
child (14 years old or below)	£1.75
adult (60 years old or above)	£1.95
monthly adult season ticket	£28.50
monthly adult season ticket (before 4 p.m. only)	£19.95
monthly child season ticket	£14.50
monthly adult (60 years old or above) season ticket	£16

Monday to Friday	
07:00 – 08:30	lane swimming only
08:30 – 09:30	lessons only
09:30 – 12:15	public swimming
12:15 – 14:00	lessons only
14:00 – 17:00	public swimming
17:00 – 18:30	life saving lessons
18:30 – 20:00	public swimming
20:00 – 21:00	women only

Saturday	Sunday
07:00 – 09:00 swimming club	07:30 – 09:30 swimming club
09:00 – 12:30 public swimming	09:30 – 12:30 public swimming
12:30 – 13:30 lane swimming only	12:30 – 14:00 lessons only
13:30 – 17:30 public swimming	14:00 – 17:00 public swimming
17:30 – 21:30 swimming club	17:00 – 21:00 swimming club

1 Charlie is 15 years old. He likes to swim in the evenings 12 times each month. How much will he save by buying a monthly season ticket?

2 Margaret is 40 years old. She swims in the morning 8 times each month. How much will she save by buying a monthly ticket?

Bus timetable				
Market Cross	08:20	every hour until	19:20
Hospital	08:28	every hour until	19:28
Town Hall	08.35	every hour until	19:35
Train Station	08.47	every hour until	19:47
Swimming Pool	09.01	every hour until	20:01

3 Every Thursday Murray catches the 09:35 bus from the Town Hall to the swimming pool. If he takes 15 minutes to pay and get changed, how long can he swim until the end of the public session?

4 Which is the latest bus from the Market Cross that Lily can catch on a Saturday if she is to be on time for the evening swimming club?

5 Every week without fail Carly attends swimming club in the morning and evening at weekends. How many hours does she spend in total at swimming club during one year (52 weeks)?

On these pages you will look at the six main four-sided shapes (quadrilaterals).

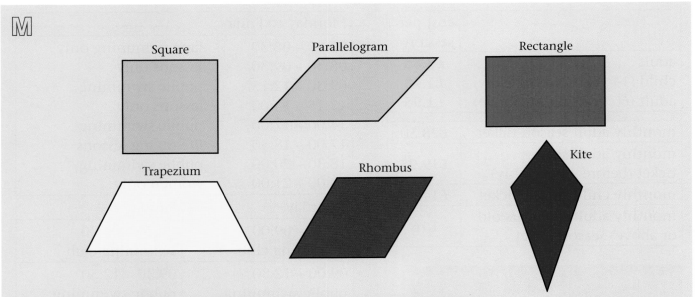

You need a ruler to measure the sides in the quadrilaterals above.

Write down which shapes have:

(1) *All* four sides equal.

(2) Two *pairs* of sides equal.

(3) Two *pairs* of sides parallel.

(4) *All* angles 90°.

(5) Two lines of symmetry *only*.

(6) One line of symmetry *only*.

(7) Rotational symmetry of *order two* (you may need to ask your teacher for a reminder).

Draw a pair of axes as shown.

For each question below, draw a cross at the three given co-ordinates.

These show three vertices (corners) of the given shape.

Use these three vertices to draw the *complete* shape and *write down the co-ordinates* of the missing vertex (corner).

(1) (1, 6) (1, 8) (2, 8) (?) rectangle

(2) (1, 3) (1, 5) (3, 5) (?) square

(3) (4, 4) (3, 7) (4, 8) (?) kite

(4) (6, 4) (6, 7) (7, 8) (?) parallelogram

(5) (4, 2) (7, 3) (6, 6) (?) square

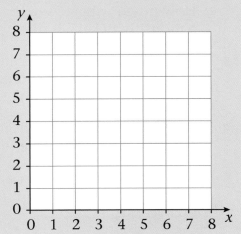

On these pages you will calculate the radius and diameter of a circle and you will use a pair of compasses to draw circles.

- The perimeter of a circle is called *circumference*.

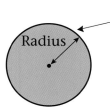 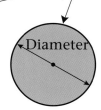

- The distance from the centre of a circle to the circumference is called *radius*.

- The distance across a circle through its centre is called *diameter*.

- The diameter is twice the radius. If we write *d* for diameter and *r* for radius then $d = 2r$

M

Find the radius and the diameter of each circle.

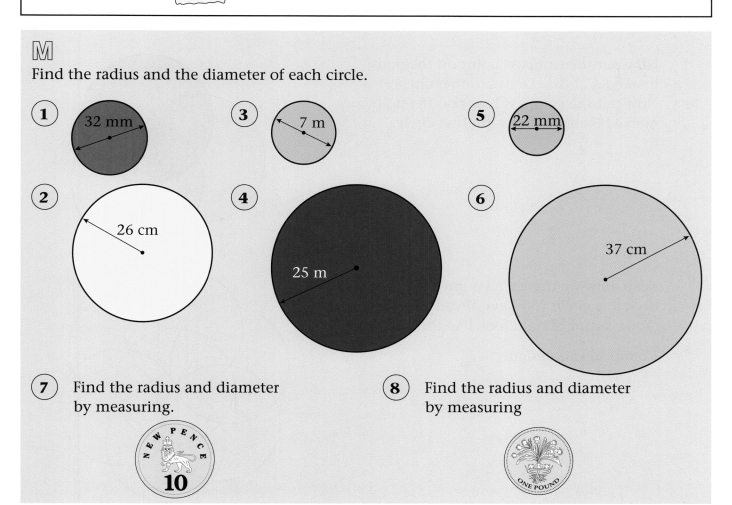

(1) 32 mm

(2) 26 cm

(3) 7 m

(4) 25 m

(5) 22 mm

(6) 37 cm

(7) Find the radius and diameter by measuring.

(8) Find the radius and diameter by measuring

You need a ruler, pencil and a pair of compasses.

1 Draw a circle with radius 5 cm.

3 Draw a circle with diameter 8 cm.

2 Draw a circle with radius 6 cm.

4 Draw a circle with diameter 6 cm.

5 Draw a circle with radius 4.5 cm. Measure and write down the diameter of this circle.

6 Draw a circle with radius 7 cm.
Inside this circle, draw another circle
with radius 5 cm. *Inside* this circle,
draw another circle with *diameter* 6 cm.

7 Draw a circle with radius 6 cm.
Put the compass point anywhere on the
circumference (DO NOT LET THE COMPASSES
'SLIP') and draw another circle.

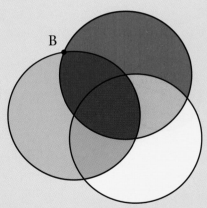

Now put the compass point on the point
marked A above. Draw another circle.
Now put the compass point on the point
marked B above. Draw another circle.

Keep drawing these circles until you get
back to a circle you have already drawn.
(Your picture should look like the one below.)

Colour in this design.

8 Repeat the Question **7** approach to draw the picture below:

Colour in this diagram.

9 Repeat the Question **7** approach to draw the picture below:

Colour in this design.

10 You can draw a regular hexagon (a shape with 6 equal sides) using compasses and a ruler only.

Draw a circle with radius 6 cm (DRAW IT FAINTLY). Put the compass point anywhere on the circumference (DO NOT LET THE COMPASSES 'SLIP') and make a little 'mark' on the circumference like opposite.

Now put the compass point on the point marked A above. Draw another mark (called an 'arc') like below.

Now put the compass point on the point marked B opposite. Draw another arc.

Keep drawing these arcs until you get back to the arc you started with.

Join up all the arcs to make a hexagon.

Colour in your '*perfect*' regular hexagon.

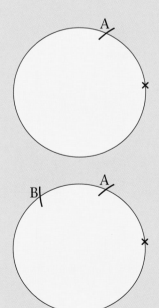

On these pages you will draw accurate triangles using a ruler and protractor only.
You will also draw triangles with a ruler and a pair of compasses only.

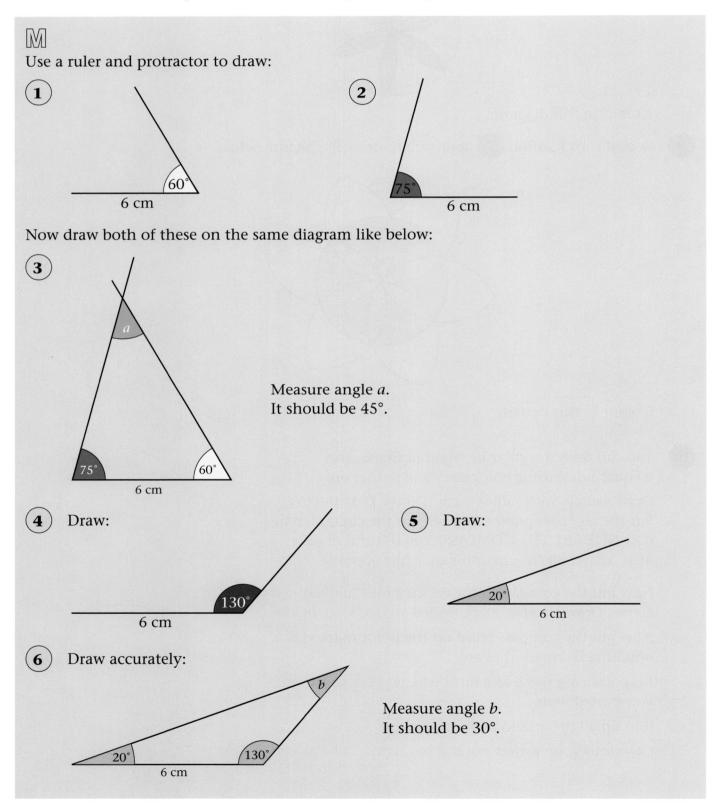

Ⓜ

Use a ruler and protractor to draw:

① 60° 6 cm

② 75° 6 cm

Now draw both of these on the same diagram like below:

③

Measure angle *a*.
It should be 45°.

75° 60° 6 cm

④ Draw: 130° 6 cm

⑤ Draw: 20° 6 cm

⑥ Draw accurately:

b

Measure angle *b*.
It should be 30°.

20° 6 cm 130°

Draw accurately the diagrams in Questions ⑦ to ⑯.

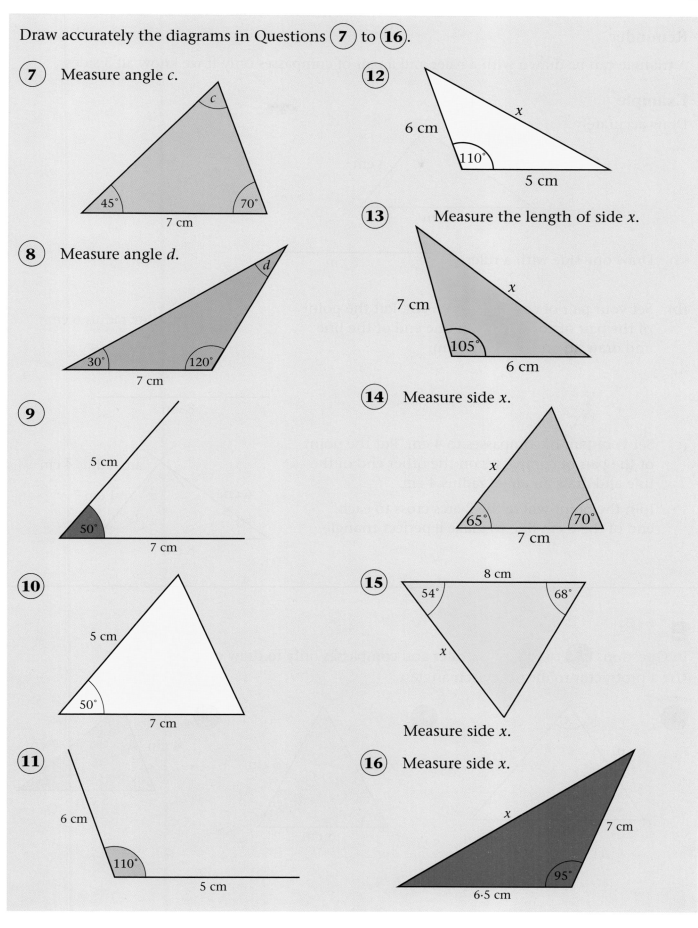

⑦ Measure angle c.

c

$45°$ $70°$

7 cm

⑧ Measure angle d.

d

$30°$ $120°$

7 cm

⑨

5 cm

$50°$

7 cm

⑩

5 cm

$50°$

7 cm

⑪

6 cm

$110°$

5 cm

⑫

x

6 cm

$110°$

5 cm

⑬ Measure the length of side x.

x

7 cm

$105°$

6 cm

⑭ Measure side x.

x

$65°$ $70°$

7 cm

⑮

8 cm

$54°$ $68°$

x

Measure side x.

⑯ Measure side x.

x

7 cm

$95°$

6·5 cm

Reminder

A triangle can be drawn with a ruler and a pair of compasses only if we know all 3 sides.

Example

Draw accurately

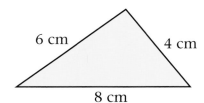

(a)   Draw one side with a ruler

8 cm

(b)   Set your pair of compasses to 6 cm. Put the point of the pair of compasses on one end of the line and draw an arc of radius 6 cm.

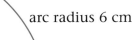

arc radius 6 cm

8 cm

(c)   Set your pair of compasses to 4 cm. Put the point of the pair of compasses on the other end of the line and draw an arc of radius 4 cm.

Join the point where the 2 arcs cross to each end of the 8 cm line to make a perfect triangle.

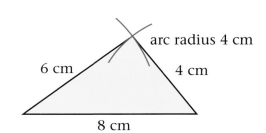

E

In Questions ❶ to ❻, use a ruler and compasses only to draw each triangle.
Use a protractor to measure each angle *x*.

1

2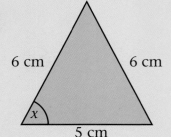

3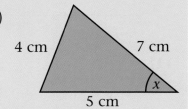

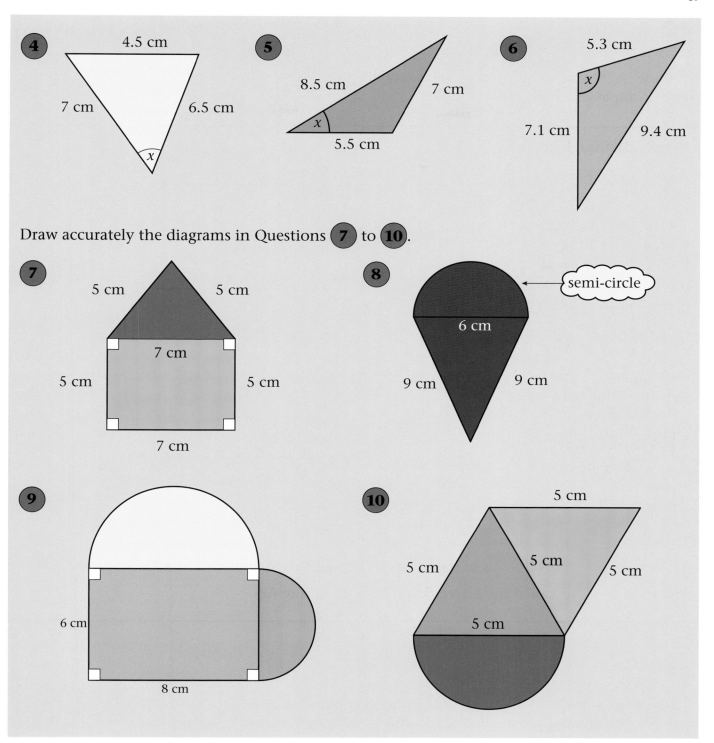

4 4.5 cm 7 cm 6.5 cm *x*

5 8.5 cm 7 cm *x* 5.5 cm

6 5.3 cm *x* 7.1 cm 9.4 cm

Draw accurately the diagrams in Questions **7** to **10**.

7 5 cm 5 cm 7 cm 5 cm 5 cm 7 cm

8 semi-circle 6 cm 9 cm 9 cm

9 6 cm 8 cm

10 5 cm 5 cm 5 cm 5 cm 5 cm

On these pages you will draw some accurate diagrams using only a pencil, a straight edge and a pair of compasses.

Perpendicular bisector

Draw a line AB 8 cm long.

Set the pair of compasses to more than 4 cm (half the line AB).
Put the compass point on A and draw an arc as shown.

Put the compass point on B ('DO NOT LET THE COMPASSES SLIP').
Draw another arc as shown.

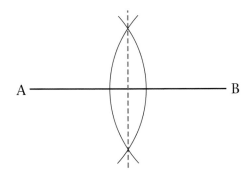

Draw a broken line as shown.

This broken line cuts line AB in half (bisects) and is at right angles to line AB (*perpendicular*).

The broken line is called the *perpendicular* bisector of line AB.

---

①   Draw a horizontal line AB of the length 6 cm.
Construct the perpendicular bisector of AB.

②   Draw a vertical line CD of length 9 cm.
Construct the perpendicular bisector of CD.

③   Draw a vertical line EF of length 7 cm.
Construct the perpendicular bisector of EF.

④   Draw a horizontal line GH of length 4 cm.
Construct the perpendicular bisector of GH.

5 (a) Use a pencil, ruler and a pair of compasses *only* to *construct* the triangle ABC shown opposite (YOU MAY NEED YOUR TEACHER TO REMIND YOU HOW TO DO THIS).

(b) *Construct* the *perpendicular* bisector of line AB.

(c) *Construct* the *perpendicular* bisector of line AC.

(d) If done accurately, your two lines from ⓑ and ⓒ should cross exactly on the line BC.

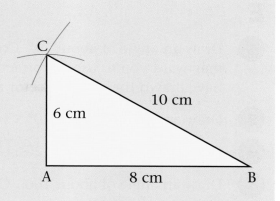

6 Draw *any* triangle KLM and construct

(a) the perpendicular bisector of KM

(b) the perpendicular bisector of KL. Mark the point of intersection X.

Take a pair of compasses and, with centre at X and radius KX, draw a circle through the points K, L and M. This is the *circumcircle of triangle KLM*.

Repeat the construction for another triangle of different shape.

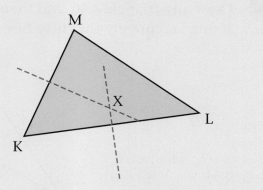

Bisector of an angle

Draw any angle as shown.

Put the compass point on A and draw an arc as shown.

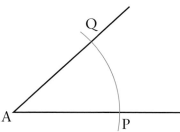

Put the compass point on P and draw an arc as shown. Put the compass point on Q and draw an arc as shown.

Draw a broken line as shown.

This broken line cuts the angle in half (bisects). This broken line is called the *angle* bisector.

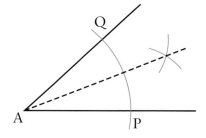

1 Draw an angle of about 70°. Construct the bisector of the angle (your teacher may want you to use a protractor to measure the angles to check that you have drawn the angle bisector accurately).

2 Draw an angle of about 40°. Construct the bisector of the angle.

3 Draw an angle of about 120°. Construct the bisector of the angle.

4 Draw an angle of about 100°. Construct the bisector of the angle.

5 Draw any triangle ABC and then construct the bisectors of angles A, B and C. If done accurately the three bisectors should all pass through one point.

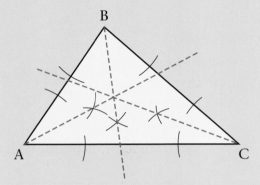

6 Draw any triangle ABC and construct the bisectors of angles B and C to meet at point Y.

With centre at Y draw a circle which just touches the sides of the triangle. This is the *inscribed circle of the triangle*.

Repeat the construction for a different triangle.

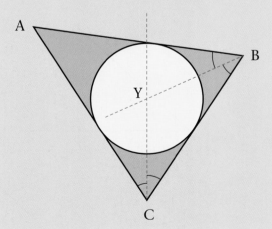

On these pages you will interpret and complete two-way tables.

This is a two-way table showing how many boys and girls are in Year 9 and Year 10

You can add up totals in two ways (across or down)

	Boys	Girls	Total
Year 9	85	95	180
Year 10	75	90	165
Total	160	185	

Grand total

(Should be the same if you add 'across' or add 'down', should be 345)

M

1 Copy and complete this two-way table.

You should get the same grand total in the corner if you add 'across' or add 'down'.

	Boys	Girls	Total
Year 8	71	58	
Year 9	87	92	
Total			

2

	Male	Female	Total
smoker	207	368	
non-smoker	342	219	
Total			

Copy and complete this two-way table.

3 Dean and Jane go skating and line-dancing. The two-way table shows how many times each went in August.

Copy and complete the two-way table.

	Dean	Jane	Total
Skating	5	8	13
Line-dancing		7	
Total	12		

4

	Snippets	Scissorbox	Total
Haircuts	38	49	87
Perms	22		
Total		100	

Snippets and Scissorbox are two hairdressing shops. The two-way table shows how many haircuts and perms they do.

Copy and complete the two-way table.

5 John and Louisa are members at the local go-carting club.

The two-way table shows the most laps completed in one hour during four different weeks.

Copy and complete the two-way table.

	John	Louisa	Total
Week 1	10	12	
Week 2	12		
Week 3	8	9	17
Week 4	9	12	
Total		44	

1 Lucy and Kylie run a shop which does body-piercing. Studs are mainly put in ears, tongues, noses and navels (belly-buttons). The table shows how many are done one week.

	Nose	Ear	Tongue	Navel	Total
Lucy	6	18	2		
Kylie	8		3	14	
Total		30		25	

(a) Copy and complete the table.

(b) How many noses are pierced each week by both Lucy and Kylie?

(c) How many ears does Kylie pierce?

(d) How many tongues are pierced in a week by both Lucy and Kylie?

(e) How many navels does Lucy pierce?

(f) How many piercings of any kind does Lucy do in the week?

2

	Jackie	Ian	Nazim	Total
Check-ups	48	58		
Fillings		73	165	
Extractions	14	9	12	35
Total	180		210	

Jackie, Ian and Nazim are dentists. Most jobs are check-ups, fillings or extractions (having a tooth pulled out). The table shows how many are done one week.

(a) Copy and complete the table.

(b) How many fillings did Jackie do in the week?

(c) How many check-ups did Nazim do in the week?

(d) How many fillings were done in total by the three dentists?

(e) How many extractions were done in total by the three dentists?

On these pages you will draw pie charts and interpret pie charts.

Reminder

A survey about favourite take-away food was done. The results are below:

Food	Frequency (number of people)
Burger	5
Chinese	4
Fish and Chips	1
Curry	7
Pizza	3

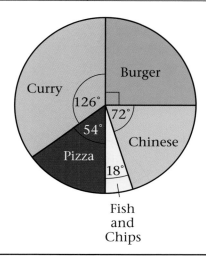

Draw a pie chart to show this information.

Method

(a) Add up all the frequency numbers:
$5 + 4 + 1 + 7 + 3 = 20$ people

(b) Whole angle in a pie chart = $360°$
This must be split between 20 people.
Angle for each person = $360° ÷ 20$
$ = 18°$

(c) Angle for 'Burger' = $5 × 18° = 90°$
Angle for 'Chinese' = $4 × 18° = 72°$
Angle for 'Fish and Chips' = $1 × 18° = 18°$
Angle for 'Curry' = $7 × 18° = 126°$
Angle for 'Pizza' = $3 × 18° = 54°$

1 A survey about favourite TV channels was done. The results are below:

TV Channel	Frequency (number of people)
ITV	11
Channel 4	2
BBC 1	8
BBC 2	4
Others	15

(a) Add up all the frequency numbers

(b) Work out the angle on a pie chart for each person
[i.e. $360° ÷$ (total number of people)]

(c) Work out the angle for each TV channel and draw a pie chart.

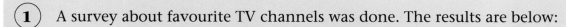

In Questions ② to ④, work out the angle for each item and draw a pie chart.

② Most popular after shool activities

Activity	Frequency
Drama	15
Sport	22
Computing	12
Art	6
Cooking	5

③ Pupils' favourite 'Disney' film

Film	Frequency
Jungle Book	34
The Lion King	18
Snow White	12
101 Dalmations	10
Others	16

④ Pupils' favourite fruit

Fruit	Frequency
Apple	25
Orange	31
Strawberry	42
Banana	18
Peach	20
Others	44

⑤ 240 people were asked about their favourite kind of shop.
The pie chart shows the results of this survey.

(a) How many people like 'Clothes' shops best?

(b) How many people like 'Shoe' shops best?

(c) How many people like 'Music' shops best?

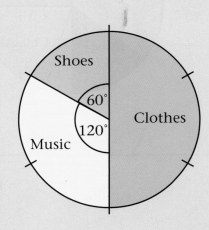

⑥

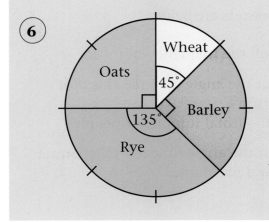

The pie chart shows the ingredients of a packet of breakfast cereal.
The packet weighs 480 g.

(a) What is the weight of the Barley?

(b) What is the weight of the Wheat?

(c) What is the weight of the Oats?

Using percentages to draw a pie chart

Example

Some people were asked what they thought the most important modern invention was.

    25% said 'Computer'
    10% said 'TV'
    15% said 'Car'
    50% said 'Telephone'

Draw a pie chart to show this information.

The whole angle is 360°
Use the percentages to find
the angle for each item.

Computer: 25% of 360° = $\frac{1}{4}$ of 360° = 90°

TV: 10% of 360° = $\frac{1}{10}$ of 360° = 36°

Telephone: 50% of 360° = $\frac{1}{2}$ of 360° = 180°

Car: 10% of 360° = 36°
    so 5% of 360° = 18°
    so 15% of 360° = 36° + 18° = 54°

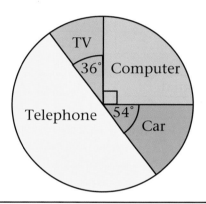

1. Some people were asked what their favourite leisure activity was.

    40% said 'Watching TV'

    20% said 'Playing sport'

    25% said 'Watching films'

    15% said 'Other things'

Use the percentages to find the angle for each item
then draw a pie chart to show this information.

In Questions **2** to **4**, use the percentages to find the angle for each item then draw a pie chart.

2 Favourite type of music.

Type of music	Percentage
Rock	45%
Jazz	15%
Classical	25%
Folk	5%
Others	10%

3 Most popular supermarket.

Supermarket	Percentage
Tesco	35%
Asda	20%
Somerfield	10%
Sainsburys	30%
Others	5%

4 Favourite football club.

Club	Percentage
Chelsea	15%
Liverpool	10%
Man. United	30%
Arsenal	25%
Newcastle United	10%
Everton	10%

5
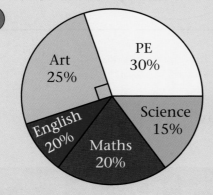

120 children at a school were asked to state their favourite subject.

The pie chart shows the results.

Write down each *subject* and how many children chose it.

6 The children at a school were asked to state their favourite sport. Here are the results.

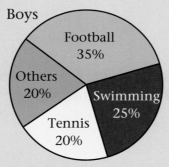

There were 80 boys

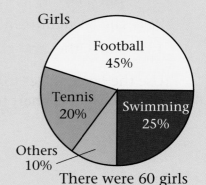

There were 60 girls

James says 'The same number of boys and girls chose tennis'.
Mel says 'More boys than girls chose swimming'.
(a) Use both charts to explain whether or not James is right.
(b) Use both charts to explain whether or not Mel is right.

Average and Range

On these pages you will find the mean, median, mode and range of data.

The mean

All the data is added and the total is divided by the number of items. In everyday language the word 'average' usually stands for the mean.

The median

When the data is arranged in order of size, the median is the one in the middle. If there are two 'middle' numbers, the median is in the middle of these two numbers.

The mode

The mode is the number or quality (like a colour) which occurs most often. Sometimes a set of data will have no mode, two modes or even more and this is a problem which we cannot avoid.

Range

The range is not an average but is the difference between the largest value and the smallest value in a set of data. It is useful in comparing sets of data when the *spread* of the data is important.

Ⓜ

① (a) Find the mean of the numbers 5, 2, 7, 9, 7
 (b) Find the median of the numbers 8, 5, 1, 3, 4, 3, 9
 (c) Find the median of the numbers 7, 2, 3, 5, 5, 3, 4, 5
 (d) Find the mode of the numbers 4, 3, 4, 4, 3, 2, 4, 3
 (e) Find the mode of the numbers 7, 1, 3, 1, 7, 8, 7, 1, 4
 (f) Find the mean of the numbers 8, 4, 1, 1, 7, 9, 6, 4

② The marks in a maths test for 12 children are:

    9   3   7   7   5   9   8   2   7   2   6   7

Work out the range, mean, median and mode.

③ King Richard (the Lionheart) was king for 10 years. 4 other kings ruled for 21 years, 16 years, 22 years and 31 years.

Work out the range, mean, median and mode for how long these 5 kings ruled.

4 The pocket money (in £) each week for 9 children is:

5 3 3 6 1 5 10 5 7

Work out the range, mean, median and mode.

E

You may use a calculator to work out the questions below:

1 (a) Find the mean of the numbers 4, 13, 5, 7, 9, 6, 5

(b) Find the median of the numbers 6, 20, 1, 16, 2, 12, 6, 3, 8, 6, 8

(c) Find the mode of the numbers 13, 2, 11, 2, 10, 4, 5, 10, 8, 10

2 In several different garages the cost of one litre of petrol is
75p, 72.8p, 76.4p, 73.1p, 79p, 73.8p, 77p.

What is the median cost of one litre of petrol?

3 Six girls have heights of 1.48 m, 1.51 m, 1.47 m, 1.55 m, 1.40 m and 1.59 m.

(a) Find the mean height of the six girls.

(b) Find the mean height of the remaining five girls when the tallest girl leaves.

4 Mrs Green gave birth to five babies (two girls and three boys) which weighed 1.3 kg,
1.2 kg, 1.45 kg, 1.35 kg and 1.3 kg. What was the median weight of the babies?

5 Sally throws a dice eight times and wins 20p if the median score is more than 3. The
dice shows 6, 1, 2, 6, 4, 1, 3, 6. Find the median score. Does she win 20p?

6 The temperature was recorded at 0400 in seven towns across the U.K.
The readings were 08, 18, –48, 18, –28, –58, –48.

What was the median temperature?

7 The test results for a class of 30 pupils were as follows:

Mark	3	4	5	6	7	8
Frequency	2	5	4	7	6	6

What was the modal mark?

8 Find the range of the following sets of numbers:

(a) 4, 11, 3, 8, 22, 5, 7, 30, 18

(b) 9, 18, 100, 64, 11, 26

(c) 4, –2, 6, 4, 5, 10, 3.

On these pages you will look at problems comparing 2 sets of data.

To compare 2 sets of data, always write at least 2 things:

1) Compare an average (i.e. mean, median or mode).

2) Compare the range of each set of data (this shows how spread out the data is).

Example

Show sizes

The Freeman family: 11   5   5   10   6

The Davidson family: 4   8   5   4   9   10

For the Freeman family: find an average, eg. mode = 5

find the range, i.e. 11 – 5 = 6

For the Davidson family: find an average, e.g. mode = 4

find the range, i.e. 10 – 4 = 6

Compare the shoe sizes of the Freeman family and the Davidson family.

Answer

The mode (*modal shoe size*) for the Freeman family is greater than the mode for the Davidson family but the range for the Freeman family is the same as the range for the Davidson family (i.e. they have the same spread).

---

1   *Shoe sizes:*

The Harris family: 8 3 6 9 6 4

The Singh family: 7 5 6 6 7 2 7

Copy and complete the statements below to compare the shoe sizes of the Harris family and the Singh family.

The Harris family: mode = _____ range = _____

The Singh family: mode = _____ range = _____

'The mode (modal shoe size) for the Harris family is (*greater/smaller*) than the mode for the Singh family and the range for the Harris family is (*greater/smaller*) than the range for the Singh family (i.e. shoe sizes for the Harris family are (*more/less*) spread out.'

(2) The weekly pocket money (in pounds) for some children is shown below:

Class 9L: 3   3   5   10   5   2   10   3   5   4

Class 9N: 5   2   5   3   1   2   4   5   5   8

Copy and complete the statements below to compare the pocket money for these children in class 9L and class 9N.

Class 9L = mean _____ range = _____

Class 9N = mean _____ range = _____

'The mean for class 9L is (*greater/smaller*) than the mean for class 9N and the range of class 9L is (*greater/smaller*) than the range of class 9N (i.e. pocket money in class 9L is (*more/less*) spread out'.

(3) Some children took a Science test. Their marks are listed below:

Class 9C: 39   72   41   43   58   77   64   49   49

Class 9D: 48   52   63   81   62   56   32   63   76   46   68

Copy and complete the statements below to compare the Science marks for the children in class 9C and class 9D.

Class 9C = median _____ range = _____

Class 9D = median _____ range = _____

'The median test score for class 9C is . . . . than the median test score for class 9D and the range of test scores for class 9C is . . . . than the range of test scores for class 9D (i.e. the test scores for class 9C are . . . . spread out).

E

(1) The Comets and the Typhoons are 2 athletic teams. They each have runners in the 100 m races.

Their best times (in seconds) are listed below:

The Comets: 10.7   10.5   11   10.8   11.2   11.1   10.9

The Typhoons: 10.9   10.4   11.1   10.7   10.6

Use the median and range to write a sentence to compare the times taken by the runners for the Comets and the Typhoons in the 100 m race.

2 18 children were asked how often they ate meat each week (10 children from Year 9 and 8 children from Year 11). The results are below:

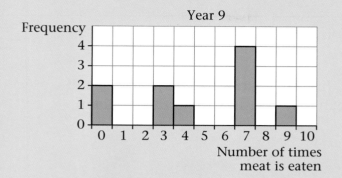

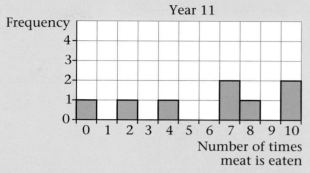

(a) Work out the mean and range for Year 9.

(b) Work out the mean and range for Year 11.

(c) Write a sentence to compare the number of times meat is eaten each week by children in Year 9 and Year 11.

3 The Warriors and the Sabres are 2 basketball teams.
The ages (in years) of the players in each team
are listed below:

The Warriors: 24   22   17   28   22   19   31   27   21   27

The Sabres: 28   24   18   20   19   30   27   19   24   18

Use the mean and range to write a sentence to compare
the ages of the players for the Warriors and the Sabres.

On these pages you will state a hypothesis, collect data, process data and interpret the data.

You are going to look at a problem where you need to collect data and use the data.
You will have to:

(1) Discuss a problem, decide what you think may be true (the hypothesis) and consider any 'related' questions (questions which may be asked about the problem).

(2) Decide which data to collect.

(3) Decide how to collect the data.

(4) Present the data using graphs and charts.

(5) Can you use the mean, median or mode?

(6) Can you use the range?

(7) Use everything you have done to show if your hypothesis is true or not.

Ⓜ

YOUR TEACHER WILL ASK YOU TO WORK THROUGH THE PROJECT BELOW *OR* TO PICK YOUR OWN TOPIC.

Task 1

TV programs can be put into the following groups:

        comedy   soaps   sports   drama   cartoons   others

(1) You will ask 20 pupils in your class what their favourite TV program is. Write down which TV group above you think will be the most popular (this will be your 'hypothesis').

(2) Are there any problems you can think of before you ask the 20 pupils about their favourite TV program?

3 You need to design a data collection sheet.
2 possible examples are given below:

Name	TV program	TV group
David	Eastenders	soap
Emma	Simpsons	cartoon
Lynne		
Narishta		

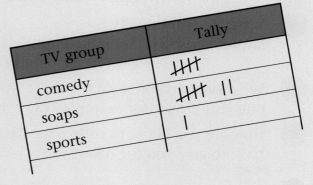

TV group	Tally
comedy	⊬⊬ ⊬⊬ ||
soaps	⊬⊬
sports		

Now ask 20 pupils in your class what their favourite TV program is.

4 Put your data in a frequency table like below:

TV groups	Frequency
comedy	
soaps	
sports	
drama	
cartoons	
others	

Remember:
'frequency' means
'how many'.

Now present the data on a chart.
Use a bar chart or a pie chart (*there is no point doing both*).
Try and do a pie chart if you think you can.
(Use a computer to make a pie chart if possible and compare it to your hand-drawn pie chart.)

5 Can you work out an average (mean, median or mode)?
In this problem, only the mode is useful (the 'mode' is the 'most popular' TV group).

6 Is there any point working out the range?
(The 'range' is the 'highest number-lowest number').
The only numbers are in the frequency table.
There is *no point* working out the range of these.

7 *Conclusion*
Look at your chart and the mode.
(a) Was your hypothesis correct?
(b) Make comments about your results.
   (for example: '3 times more people liked cartoons than drama')
(c) Write down anything else about doing this problem that you feel is useful.

E   **Task 2**

Are absences from school equally likely on any day of the week?

1   What do you think?
Related Questions: Are more pupils absent on Mondays and Fridays than other days?
Do Year 11 pupils take more days off school than Year 7 pupils?

2   What data do you need to collect? Are you going to look at the whole school or just one year group (for example Year 9 only).

3   How are you going to collect the data? From school records? Your teacher will probably have to give you the data.

4   At this stage, you *must* show your teacher your main hypothesis and tell your teacher exactly what data you are going to record.

5   Now present the data on a chart.

For example:

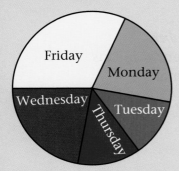

Number of pupils in
Year 9 absent each day

Number of pupils in
Year 9 absent each day

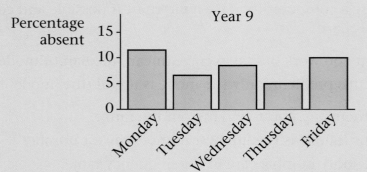

6   Can you use mean, median, mode or range for any of your data? (For example: the mean average number of absences per day for Year 9 pupils). *Discuss with your teacher.*

7   *Conclusion*

Look at your charts and averages.

(a) Was your main hypothesis correct?

(b) Make comments about your results. (for example: 'A higher percentage of Year 11 pupils were absent on Mondays than Year 9 pupils'.)

(c) Write down anything else about doing this problem that you feel is useful.

On these pages you will interpret information given in tables, graphs and charts.

Ⓜ

①

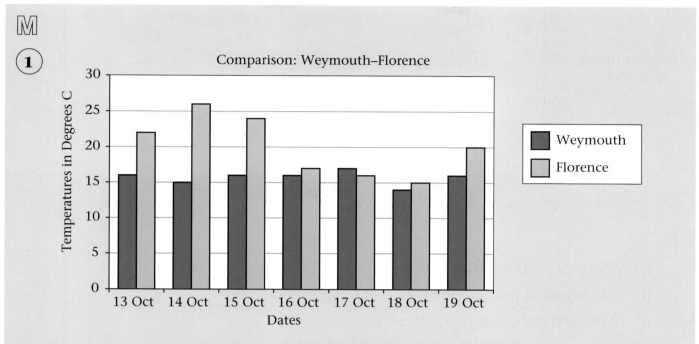

Comparison: Weymouth–Florence

(a) On which day was it warmer in Weymouth than in Florence?

(b) Which day was the warmest in Florence?

(c) Which was the coldest day in Weymouth?

(d) On how many days was it 20° C or more in Florence?

(e) On how many days was it 15° C or lower in Weymouth?

(f) On which day was the difference in temperatures the greatest?

② The graph shows a train journey taken by Amy from England to France to visit her parents.

(a) When did the journey start in England?

(b) How long was the wait in London?

(c) How long did it take to go from London to Paris?

(d) How long was the wait in Paris?

(e) What time did the train leave London?

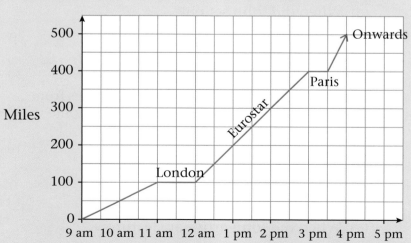

3

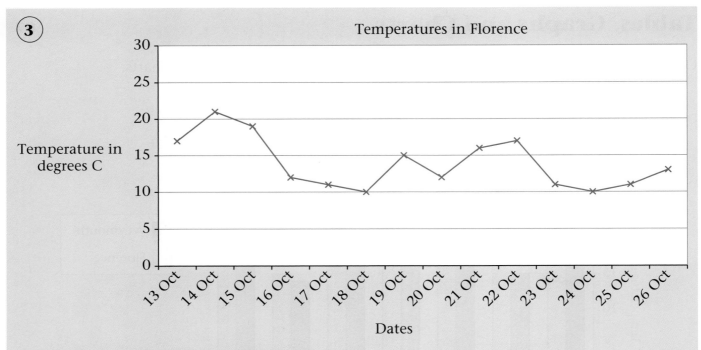

Temperatures in Florence

(a) Which day was the warmest?

(b) Roughly what temperature was it on the warmest day?

(c) Give the dates of the two coldest days.

(d) What was the temperature on the two coldest days?

(e) What was the drop in temperature between the 19th and 24th of October?

(f) What was the temperature on the 19th October?

E

The graph shows John's trip to Heathrow Airport to collect his mother. On the way there he was stuck in traffic on the M25.

(a) When did John set out?

(b) How long was he stuck in traffic?

(c) How far was John's journey to Heathrow altogether?

(d) How long did he spend at the airport?

(e) When did he arrive home?

(f) How long was his return journey?

(g) When did John arrive at Heathrow?

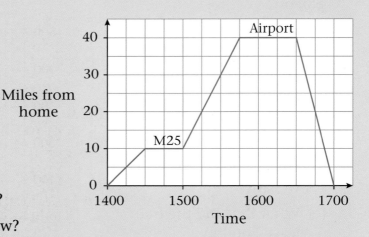

2 This chart shows the distances in km by road between some of the cities of Britain.

Birmingham	Bristol	Cardiff	Edinburgh	Glasgow	Leeds	Liverpool	Manchester	Newcastle	London
140									
163	69								
458	584	589							
458	584	592	70						
174	310	333	306	336					
144	256	262	336	340	117				
126	255	275	336	338	64	56			
320	454	477	170	229	146	245	205		
176	186	245	597	627	304	315	294	140	

How far is it in km from:

(a) Birmingham to London?

(b) Bristol to Glasgow?

(c) Leeds to London?

(d) Cardiff to Edinburgh?

(e) Newcastle to Birmingham?

(f) Which is longer: Birmingham to Newcastle or Edinburgh to Liverpool?

(g) How far is the journey from Birmingham to Cardiff and then on to London.

(h) Which two cities are farthest apart?

(i) Jack drives from Cardiff to Newcastle then back again. How far does he travel in total?

On this page you will learn how to use brackets, divide, multiply, add and subtract in the correct order.

Remember the word 'BODMAS'.

Examples

(a) $7 + 2 \times 4$
  $= 7 + 8$
  $= 15$

(b) $(3 + 2) \times (4 + 2)$
  $= 5 \times 6$
  $= 30$

B rackets first
O
D ivide
M ultiply   in this order
A dd
S ubtract

M

Work out:

(1) $2 + 3 \times 4$
(2) $4 + 2 \times 6$
(3) $5 + 3 \times 2$
(4) $6 + 6 \times 4$
(5) $8 + 2 \times 3$

(6) $6 \times 3 + 2$
(7) $10 \times 2 + 8$
(8) $3 \times 7 + 3$
(9) $12 \times 6 + 2$
(10) $15 \times 2 + 2$

(11) $12 \div 3 + 1$
(12) $15 \div 3 + 2$
(13) $36 \div 3 + 9$
(14) $50 \div 2 + 3$
(15) $60 \div 15 + 5$

(16) $10 + 10 \div 2$
(17) $8 + 4 \div 2$
(18) $30 + 6 \div 3$
(19) $35 + 14 \div 7$
(20) $80 + 20 \div 10$

Work out:

(21) $(9 + 16) - 5$
(22) $(3 + 5) \times (4 + 2)$
(23) $(5 + 6) \times (3 + 4)$

(24) $(10 + 2) \times (4 + 2)$
(25) $(4 + 5) \times (4 + 5)$
(26) $(9 + 5) \div (4 + 3)$

(27) $(7 + 11) - (6 + 3)$
(28) $(15 + 6) \div (5 + 2)$
(29) $(19 + 6) \div (3 + 2)$

E

Work out:

(1) $4 + 2 \times 3 + 2$
(2) $1 + 93 + 4$
(3) $2 + 4 \times 5 + 3$
(4) $5 + 3 \times 2 + 10$
(5) $6 + 6 \times 4 + 5$
(6) $8 + 10 \div 2 + 3$
(7) $12 + 12 \div 4 + 2$
(8) $12 + 24 \div 6 + 2$

(9) $3 + 5 + 2 \times 4$
(10) $7 + 3 + 2 \times 3$
(11) $8 + 4 + 3 \times 2$
(12) $4 \times 6 + 1$
(13) $6 \times 2 + 2$
(14) $35 \div 5 + 2$
(15) $24 \div 8 + 4$
(16) $36 \div 6 + 3$

(17) $3 \times 2 + 5 \times 4$
(18) $6 \times 5 + 5 \times 3$
(19) $8 \times 2 + 3 \times 6$
(20) $10 \times 8 + 2 \times 5$
(21) $12 \times 2 + 2 \times 8$
(22) $48 \div 6 + 12 \div 2$
(23) $50 \div 5 + 60 \div 12$
(24) $49 \div 7 + 14 \div 2$

Addition and Subtraction

On this page you will practise addition and subtraction.

M

Copy and complete by writing the missing number in the box.

(1) 47 added to ☐ is 100.

(2) ☐ plus 61 is 134.

(3) 0.4 increased by ☐ is 1.

(4) The sum of ☐ and 360 is 630.

(5) 600 greater than ☐ is 1395.

(6) 2.3 and ☐ added together is 5.8.

(7) The total of ☐ and 39 is 114.

(8) 130 more than ☐ is 775.

(9) 250 add ☐ is 1000.

(10) 6.5 plus ☐ is 10.

(11) 5.8 increased by ☐ is 6.

(12) The total of 747 and ☐ is 800.

Work out

(13) Take 550 from 1000.

(14) 57 less than 63.

(15) 94 subtract 39.

(16) 144 decreased by 53.

(17) 8000 take away 7991.

(18) 7 less than 5000.

(19) Subtract 21 from 157.

(20) 120 take away 50.

(21) Decrease 401 by 395.

(22) Take 34 from 100.

(23) 700 less than 1500.

(24) 77 subtract 34.

E

Copy and complete by writing the missing number in the box.

(1) $4.68 + ☐ = 5$

(2) $2700 + ☐ = 5600$

(3) $0.72 + ☐ = 0.92$

(4) $4400 + ☐ = 8100$

(5) $4.37 + ☐ = 4.4$

(6) $1.3 + ☐ = 2.67$

(7) $☐ + 3600 = 8400$

(8) $☐ + 0.31 = 7$

(9) $☐ + 2.9 = 57$

(10) $☐ + 0.06 = 0.26$

(11) $☐ + 2.1 = 8.3$

(12) $☐ + 0.5 = 0.89$

Copy and complete by writing the missing number in the box.

(13) ☐ take away 8.3 is 0.7.

(14) 1.0 take away ☐ is 0.6.

(15) ☐ subtract 61 is 774.

(16) 583 subtract ☐ is 343.

(17) ☐ is 49 more than 533.

(18) 0.52 is ☐ more than 0.15.

(19) ☐ decreased by 187 is 115.

(20) 10 decreased by ☐ is 6.3.

(21) ☐ take away 2996 is 2007.

(22) 820 take away ☐ is 250.

(23) ☐ is 600 less than 1325.

(24) 7.2 is ☐ less than 9.1.

On this page you will practise short/long multiplication and short/long division.

Ⓜ
Work out using any method:

(1)	7 × 9	(4)	9 × 8	(7)	21 × 6	(10)	123 × 5
(2)	8 × 6	(5)	8 × 8	(8)	39 × 7	(11)	252 × 4
(3)	5 × 6	(6)	6 × 7	(9)	38 × 7	(12)	316 × 8

(13)	165 × 23	(16)	519 × 35	(19)	4231 × 24	(22)	505 × 43
(14)	238 × 17	(17)	774 × 52	(20)	356 × 44	(23)	820 × 34
(15)	476 × 31	(18)	761 × 29	(21)	901 × 36	(24)	359 × 41

(25)	36 ÷ 9	(28)	72 ÷ 9	(31)	327 ÷ 3	(34)	402 ÷ 6
(26)	54 ÷ 6	(29)	28 ÷ 4	(32)	288 ÷ 4	(35)	584 ÷ 8
(27)	42 ÷ 7	(30)	30 ÷ 6	(33)	329 ÷ 7	(36)	1088 ÷ 8

Ⓔ
Work out using any method:

(1)	630 ÷ 14	(4)	621 ÷ 23	(7)	945 ÷ 35
(2)	462 ÷ 21	(5)	462 ÷ 33	(8)	624 ÷ 24
(3)	826 ÷ 14	(6)	966 ÷ 42	(9)	768 ÷ 32

(10) $\begin{array}{r} 3.4 \\ \times\ \ 6 \\ \hline \end{array}$	(13) $\begin{array}{r} 6.3 \\ \times\ \ 8 \\ \hline \end{array}$	(16) $\begin{array}{r} 4.52 \\ \times\ \ 4 \\ \hline \end{array}$	(19) $\begin{array}{r} 8.91 \\ \times\ \ 2 \\ \hline \end{array}$
(11) $\begin{array}{r} 2.5 \\ \times\ \ 7 \\ \hline \end{array}$	(14) $\begin{array}{r} 4.7 \\ \times\ \ 5 \\ \hline \end{array}$	(17) $\begin{array}{r} 5.62 \\ \times\ \ 3 \\ \hline \end{array}$	(20) $\begin{array}{r} 6.79 \\ \times\ \ 5 \\ \hline \end{array}$
(12) $\begin{array}{r} 4.6 \\ \times\ \ 3 \\ \hline \end{array}$	(15) $\begin{array}{r} 7.2 \\ \times\ \ 4 \\ \hline \end{array}$	(18) $\begin{array}{r} 4.37 \\ \times\ \ 3 \\ \hline \end{array}$	(21) $\begin{array}{r} 7.62 \\ \times\ \ 6 \\ \hline \end{array}$

(22)	5.1 ÷ 3	(25)	37.2 ÷ 2	(28)	58.03 ÷ 7
(23)	13.6 ÷ 4	(26)	38.4 ÷ 8	(29)	43.12 ÷ 8
(24)	31.5 ÷ 5	(27)	65.7 ÷ 9	(30)	43.61 ÷ 7

PART ONE

(1) Work out:

(a) $\frac{1}{8}$ of £32   (b) $\frac{1}{6}$ of £54   (c) $\frac{5}{7}$ of £56   (d) $\frac{2}{9}$ of £36

(2) Copy and complete the equivalent fractions:

(a) $\frac{1}{2} = \frac{\square}{12}$ (b) $\frac{2}{3} = \frac{20}{\square}$ (c) $\frac{7}{8} = \frac{\square}{40}$ (d) $\frac{36}{54} = \frac{2}{\square}$

(3) John and Darryl are very greedy. They eat $\frac{5}{8}$ of a large cake by themselves. What fraction of the cake is left?

(4) Arrange these decimals in order. Write the smallest first.

> 6.4   6.22   6.24   6.44   6.42

(5) Arrange these decimals in order. Write the smallest first.

> 4.7   4   4.69   4.8   4.17

(6) Work out:

(a) 10% of £90   (b) 5% of £160   (c) 3% of £150

(7) *Increase £80 by 15%.*

(8) A pair of shoes are *reduced* in price from £50 by 5%. What is the new price of the shoes?

(9) Shapes are made from matchsticks as follows:

  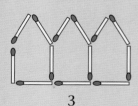

Shape number: 1   2   3

(a) Draw the next 2 shapes.

(b) How many extra sticks are needed each time?

(c) How many sticks are needed for shape number 10?

94

10 Will and Rachel share £360 in the ratio 2:7. How much money do they each get?

11 8 bars of chocolate cost £3.36. How much will 5 bars of chocolate cost?

12 The table shows the lengths of some rivers to the nearest km.

River	Length in km to the nearest km	Length in km to the nearest 100 km	Length in km to the nearest 10 km
Wye	215		
Trent	297		
Severn	354		
Dee	113		
Thames	346		

(a) Copy and complete the table.

(b) Which two rivers have the same length to the nearest 100 km?

(c) Which two rivers have the same length to the nearest 10 km?

13 Work out:

(a) $3^2 + 4^2$ (b) $\sqrt{64} + \sqrt{49}$ (c) $9^2 - \sqrt{100}$

14 Find the perimeter of the following shapes:

(a)

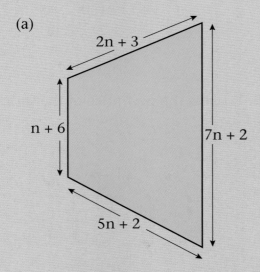

(b)

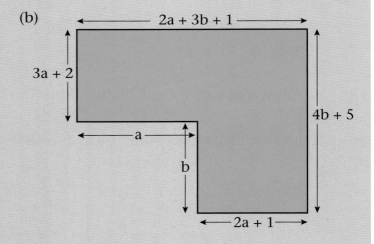

15 Solve:

(a) $5n + 3 = 23$ (b) $8n - 2 = 46$

PART TWO

(1) (a) Decrease 501 by 394.   (b) Subtract 42 from 167.

(2) Copy and complete by writing the missing number in the box:

(a) The sum of ⬜ and 280 is 730.

(b) 540 take away ⬜ is 250.

(3) Work out:

(a) 38 × 26   (b) 342 × 47   (c) 336 ÷ 7   (d) 756 ÷ 42

(4) Find the angles marked with the letters:

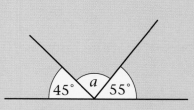 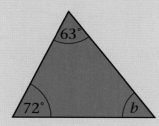 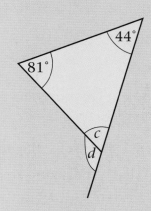

(5) (a) Draw accurately the two triangles below:

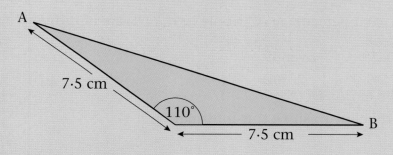 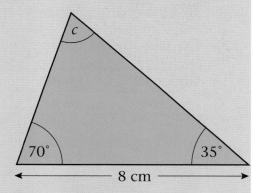

(b) Measure the length *AB*.

(c) Measure angle *c*.

(6) Work out:

(a) 4 + 6 × 3   (b) (4 + 6) × 3

(c) Copy the sum below but write in brackets so that the sum makes the given answer,

$$6 \times 3 + 5 = 48$$

(7) (a) Copy and complete this two-way table.

(b) How many girls are there in Year 9?

(c) How many children are there in total?

	Boys	Girls	Total
Year 8	75		170
Year 9			155
Total	160		

8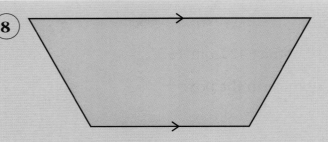

Two statements below are correct. Write down the 2 correct statements.

(a) The shape is a quadrilateral.

(b) The shape is a kite.

(c) The shape is a pentagon.

(d) The shape is a trapezium.

(e) The shape is a parallelogram.

9 For each list of numbers below, work out the range, mean, median and mode:

(a) 7, 2, 8, 8, 2, 5, 8, 16

(b) 16, 22, 23, 18, 15, 15, 23, 21, 23, 19

10

| 1 | 2 | 8 | ? | ? |

Look at the numbers above. Write down the missing numbers so that the range is 10 and the median is 6.

11 (a) A shop sells magazines.

Each magazine costs £1.49.

What is the cost of four magazines?

(b) How many magazines can you buy with £12?

12 The table below shows roughly what percentage of people in the UK are of different ages.

under 15	15–39	40–59	over 59
20%	35%	25%	20%

Copy and complete the pie chart below to show this information.

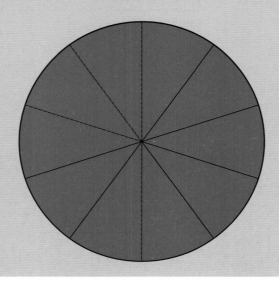

Label each section of your pie chart clearly with the ages.

Clues across

1. 4×19
3. 31×4
6. $167 + 41$
8. 6×7
9. 11.6×10
12. $123 - 85$
14. $928 + 45$
16. $530 \div 10$
18. $2004 - 1989$
19. $401 - 299$

Clues down

1. 8×9
2. $542 + 59$
4. 6×4
5. 85×5
7. 9^2
10. 9×7
11. $224 - 33$
13. 8.5×100
15. $300 \div 4$
17. $2 \times 2 \times 2 \times 2 \times 2$

Clues across

1. $413 - 61$
3. 0.68×100
5. $3 \times 3 \times 3 \times 3$
6. 12^2
7. $980 \div 2$
8. $1003 - 985$
10. $472 + 256$
11. $712 - 618$
12. $4006 - 2994$

Clues down

1. $770 \div 2$
2. 17×3
3. 80×8
4. $173 - 89$
6. 0.19×100
7. $5002 - 121$
8. $600 \div 5$
9. 9×49
10. $355 \div 5$

Clues across

1. $311 - 92$
4. $275 \div 5$
6. $7001 - 347$
8. 0.069×1000
9. 188×2
11. $422 - 53$
12. 21^2
14. $312 - 215$
16. 30×25
17. 1.28×50

Clues down

1. 38×7
2. 13^2
3. 50×1.9
5. $358 + 178$
7. 54.5×8
10. $10\,003 - 2007$
11. $(366 + 254) \div 2$
12. $(9 \times 8) - 25$
13. $360 \div 8$
15. 0.37×200

Co-ordinates and midpoints of lines

On these pages you will plot co-ordinates and find the co-ordinates of the midpoints of lines.

Example

Plot the points below and join them up in order.

a) (2, 4) (8, 1) (6, 3) (4, 4)
    (2, 6) (2, 4), (0, 3), (6, 2)

b) (5, $3\frac{1}{2}$), (4, 5), ($3\frac{1}{4}$, $4\frac{2}{3}$).

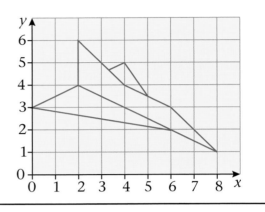

Ⓜ   Plot the points given and join them up in order. Write on the grid what the picture is.

① Draw *x* and *y* axes with values from 0 to 14.

> a) (6, 13) (1, 3) (2, 1) (12, 1) (8, 9) (6, 5)
>   (4, 5) (8, 13) (6, 13) (8, 13) (13, 3) (12, 1).

> b) (1, 3) (9, 3) (7, 7) (6, 5) (8, 5).

Now colour in the shape.

② Draw *x* and *y* axes with values from 0 to 10.

> a) (3, 2) (4, 2) (5, 3) (3, 5) (3, 6) (2, 7) (1, 6)
>   (1, 8) (2, 9) (3, 9) (5, 7) (4, 6) (4, 5) (6, 4)
>   (8, 4) (8, 5) (6, 7) (5, 7).

> b) (7, 4) (9, 2) (8, 1) (7, 3) (5, 3).

> c) (1, 6) (2, 8) (2, 9) (2, 7).

> d) Draw a dot at (3, 8).
>   Colour in the shape.

③ Draw x and y axes with values from 0 to 16.

a) (4, 9) (1, 11) (3, 8) (1, 5) (4, 7) (6, 5) (7, 5) (8, 3)
(9, 5) (11, 5) (12, 7) (15, 9) (15, 10) (12, 11) (9, 11)
(8, 14) (7, 11) (6, 11) (4, 9).

b) (15, 12) (16, 12) (16, 13) (15, 13) (15, 12).

c) (14, 14) (13, 14) (13, 15) (14, 15) (14, 14).

d) (12, 8) (13, 8).

e) Draw a dot at (13, 10). Colour in the shape.

④ Draw x and y axes with values from —7 to 10 as shown.

a) (–2, –6) (–1, –1) (–1, –4) (0, –5)
(–1, –5) (–2, –6)

b) (1, 4) (1, 1) (3, 3) (4, 5) (4, 8)

c) (–5, 7) (–6, 7) (–6, 8) (–5, 8)

d) (5, –6) (4, –5) (3, –5) (3, –3) (2, –1) (1, 0) (1, 3)
(1, 4) (2, 6) (4, 8) (3, 10) (1, 10) (0, 9) (–3, 9)
(–5, 8) (–5, 7) (–4, 6) (–2, 6) (–1, 5) (–3, 0) (–3, –5)
(–4, –5) (–5, –6) (7, –6)

e) (1, 9) (1, 8)

f) (–2, –6) (–1, 6)

Now colour in the shape.

⑤ Design your own coordinates picture.

E

1. Draw *x* and *y* axes with values from −7 to 7 as shown.

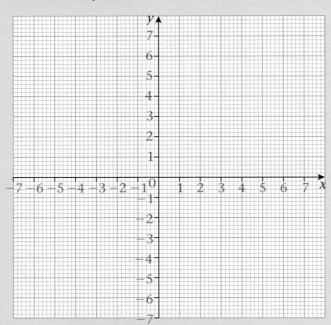

Plot and join up each set of points below. Write the letter inside the shape.

A (2, 1) (3, 1) (3, −3) (2, −3) (2, 1)

B (3, 4) (2, 6) (−2, 6) (−3, 4) (3, 4)

C (2, −5) (−1, −6) (−2, −5) (−1, −4) (2, −5)

D (7, 1) (5, 1) (4, 1) (6, −1) (7, 1)

E (1, 1) (−1, −1) (−3, 1) (−1, 3) (1, 1)

F (−1, −2) (−3, −4) (−7, −4) (−5, −2) (−1, −2)

Write down the name of each of the shapes A to F.

2.

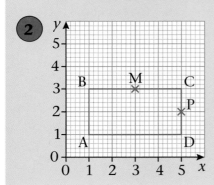

a) M is the *midpoint* (middle) of side BC. Write down the co-ordinates of M.

b) P is the *midpoint* (*middle*) *of side CD*. Write down the co-ordinates of P.

3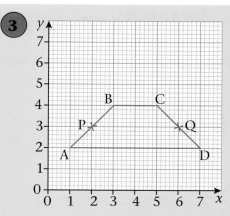

a) P is the *midpoint (middle)* of side AB.
   Write down the co-ordinates of P.

b) Q is the *midpoint (middle)* of side CD.
   Write down the co-ordinates of CD.

c) Write down the co-ordinates of the *midpoint* of side BC.

d) Write down the co-ordinates of the *midpoint* of side AD.

4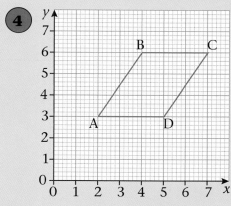

Write down the co-ordinates of the *midpoints* of each side of the parallelogram ABCD.

(You should write down 4 sets of co-ordinates.)

5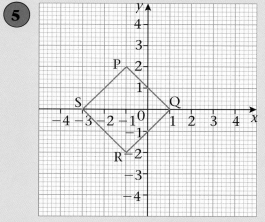

Write down the co-ordinates of the *midpoints* of each side of the square PQRS.

6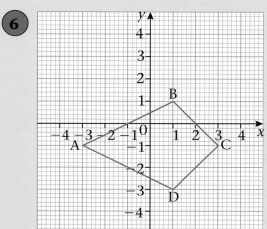

Write down the co-ordinates of the *midpoints* of each side of the kite ABCD.

On these pages you will convert one metric unit to another and solve problems using metric units.

length	mass	capacity
10 mm = 1 cm	1000 g = 1 kg	1000 ml = 1 litre
100 cm = 1 m	1000 kg = 1 tonne	
1000 m = 1 km	(1t)	

Examples

2000 m = 2 km	0.87 m = 87 cm	1.8 l = 1800 ml
2500 m = 2.5 km	2719 g = 2.719 kg	2250 g = 2.25 kg

Ⓜ

Write down which metric unit you would use to measure the following:

(1) The length of an ant.

(2) The amount of water in a swimming pool.

(3) The distance from London to Paris.

(4) The capacity of a car's petrol tank.

(5) The mass of a lorry.

(6) Write each length in cm.
   a) 3 m   b) 1.8 m   c) 20 mm   d) 0.4 m

(7) Write each length in km.
   a) 5000 m   b) 2300 m   c) 650 m   d) 100 000 m

(8) Write each mass in g.
   a) 2 kg   b) 1.65 kg   c) 0.7 kg   d) 0.085 kg

(9) Write each mass in kg.
   a) 2 tonnes   b) 50 tonnes   c) 5500 g   d) 600 g

Copy and complete.

(10) 3 m = ☐ cm   (15) 8 cm = ☐ mm   (20) 800 g = ☐ kg   (25) 2.5 m = ☐ cm

(11) 1.5 km = ☐ m   (16) 60 cm = ☐ m   (21) 8 tonnes = ☐ kg   (26) 8.7 m = ☐ cm

(12) 7 kg = ☐ g   (17) 2 m = ☐ cm   (22) 2.6 kg = ☐ g   (27) 58 mm = ☐ cm

(13) 500 g = ☐ kg   (18) 0.6 m = ☐ cm   (23) 3 litres = ☐ ml   (28) 0.45 kg = ☐ g

(14) 30 mm = ☐ cm   (19) 1.2 kg = ☐ g   (24) 32 litres = ☐ ml   (29) 8 g = ☐ kg

E

1. George swims 4 km every day. The pool is 50 m in length. How many lengths does he swim in one week?

2. Seema cut 68 cm from 2 m of string. She then cut a further 35 cm. How much string is left?

3. A rectangular field is 1586 m long and 234 m wide. How long is the fence around it in kilometres?

4. A car travels 25 m every second. How far does it travel in kilometres in five minutes?

5. A carpenter needs sixteen 40 cm lengths of wood. How many metres of wood does he need to order?

6. In June a plant grew 1.5 metres. On average how much did it grow each day? Give your answer in millimetres. [30 days in June.]

7. 150 Oxo cubes weigh 0.9 kg. What does one Oxo cube weigh in grams?

8. Mrs. Gregg receives two parcels. One weighs 380 g. The other is twice as heavy.

   What is their combined weight in kilograms?

9. A loaf of bread weighs one kilogram. It contains 25 slices.

   What does each slice weigh in grams?

10. A shelf has 46 paperback books, each weighing 200 g.

    How much weight is the shelf supporting in kilograms?

11. 4 identical containers are loaded onto a lorry. Their combined weight is 2.74 t. What is the weight of each container in kilograms?

12. A ship has 4.2 tonnes of cargo in the hold. 1368 kg is removed. How much cargo is left?

13. Eight 350 ml beakers are filled from a full 4.5 litre flask of tea. How much tea in ml is left in the flask?

14. How many 200 ml cartons of milk can be filled from a 10 litre churn?

15. There are 12 bottles of wine in a box. Each bottle contains 70 cl. How much wine is there altogether in litres?

16. A petrol pump delivers 400 ml of petrol every second. How many litres of petrol will it deliver in one minute?

Max is 14 next month. He wants to have a party in a local hall. The hire cost of the hall is shown below.

Sunday to Thursday	£6 for every 10 people
Friday/Saturday	£12 for every 22 people

The party will start with food. People can sit around a table as shown below.

● one person

The tables are laid out in the hall as shown below.

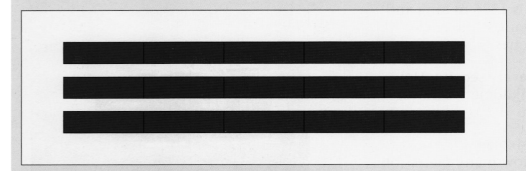

Everyone at the party must be able to sit down for the food.

Part A

1 If every seat is used, how many people can come to the party?

2 If all these people come to the party on a Friday night, how much will Max have to pay to hire the hall?

For this party Max needs to buy the food listed below:

22 pizzas	15 packets of cherry tomatoes
15 dips	11 packets of crisps
11 packets of bread sticks	100 chocolate brownies
5 kg grapes	66 cupcakes
16 packets of sausages	15 bottles of cola
10 packets of salad leaves	15 bottles of lemonade

The prices of food in 3 supermarkets is shown below:

Sureway	
pizza	£2.99
dip	£1.40
breadsticks	99p per packet
grapes	£3.25 per kg
sausages	£1.85 per packet
salad leaves	£1.75 per packet
cherry tomatoes	£1.65 per packet
crisps	£1.49 per packet
chocolate brownies (packet of 10)	£2.10 per packet
cupcakes (packet of 6)	£1.25 per packet
cola	£1.50 per bottle
lemonade	£1.40 per bottle

Fairbuy	
grapes	£2.95 per kg
cherry tomatoes	£1.70 per packet
crisps	£1.35 per packet
cola	£1.35 per bottle
sausages	£2.15 per packet
breadsticks	£1.10 per packet
lemonade	£1.15 per bottle
dip	£1.25
cupcakes (packet of 6)	99p per packet
pizza	£2.49
salad leaves	£1.65 per packet
chocolate brownies (packet of 10)	£2 per packet

Soundtrade	
lemonade	£1.20 per bottle
salad leaves	£1.95 per packet
breadsticks	£1.05 per packet
dip	£1.15
chocolate brownies (packet of 10)	£1.85 per packet
cola	£1.55 per bottle
pizza	£2.35
crisps	£1.25 per packet
sausages	£1.95 per packet
cherry tomatoes	£1.60 per packet
grapes	£3 per kg
cupcakes (packet of 6)	£1.40 per packet

Part B

Max only has time to shop for all the food in one supermarket. Which shop will be the cheapest and how much will Max spend if he shops in this supermarket?

When the tables have been put away, Max needs music. To decide on the best music, he asks 50 friends what their favourite music is. Their answers are recorded below:

D = dance   M = metal   R = R & B

H = Hip Hop   P = pop

M	D	H	M	D	R	H	M	P	H
H	D	M	D	M	P	D	D	P	M
R	M	H	D	R	H	D	M	H	D
D	D	M	H	M	H	P	R	M	D
M	H	D	H	D	M	H	H	D	P

Part C

Max thinks that the most popular music is 'Dance'. Is Max correct?

Show exactly why you think this is the answer.

Max knows 3 people who can offer the music. Max wants music for 4 hours. The cost of each person is shown below.

Dan's Rave	Kilo's Beam	Jedgroove
£25 plus £2.50 for every 6 people at the party	£35 plus £6 per hour	£72 for the whole party

Part D

1. Who is the cheapest? (remember to look at your answer to part A)

2. Who is the most expensive?

3. What is the difference in the cost of the cheapest and the most expensive?

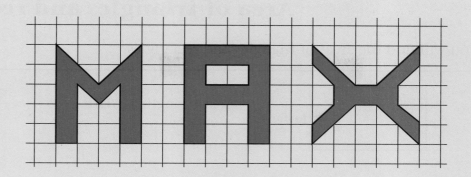

Part E

Max wants to make a big poster with his name.

He enlarges each letter above by a scale factor 2.

What is the *new* total area of the 3 letters if each small square is 4cm²?

Tina, Marvin and Rory live close to each other on the same street. After the party they each take a different taxi to get home. Each journey is 8km and the cost of each taxi is shown below.

Sam's Cab
£4 plus
80p per km

Roy's Cars
£3 plus
£1 per km

Kate's taxis
£3.50 plus
90p per km

Tina takes Sam's Cab.
It leaves the hall at 10:53 p.m. and gets Tina home in 48 minutes.

Marvin takes Roy's Cars.
It leaves the hall at 11:04 p.m. and gets Marvin home in 36 minutes.

Rory takes Kate's taxis.
It leaves the hall at 10:58 p.m. and gets Rory home in 45 minutes.

Part F

Who gets home first and who pays the least money for the taxi? Your *must* show all your working out.

On these pages you will find the areas of triangles and rectangles.

Reminder
Rectangle

Area = length × width
A = lw

Triangle

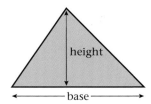

Area = (base × height) ÷ 2
This can be written as
Area = ½ (base × height)
A = ½ bh

Examples

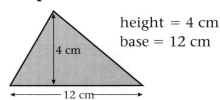

height = 4 cm
base = 12 cm

Area of triangle = ½ bh
= ½ × 12 × 4
= 6 × 4 = 24 cm²

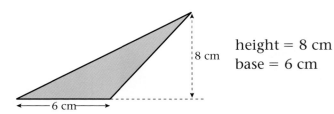

height = 8 cm
base = 6 cm

Area = ½ bh
= ½ × 6 × 8
= 3 × 8 = 24 cm²

M

In Questions **1** to **12**, find the area of each shape.

All lengths are in cm.

1

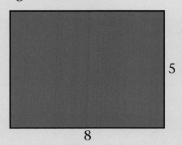

5

8

3

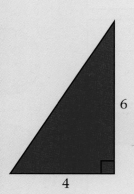

6

4

2   0.5

10

4

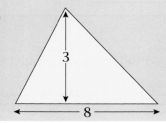

3

8

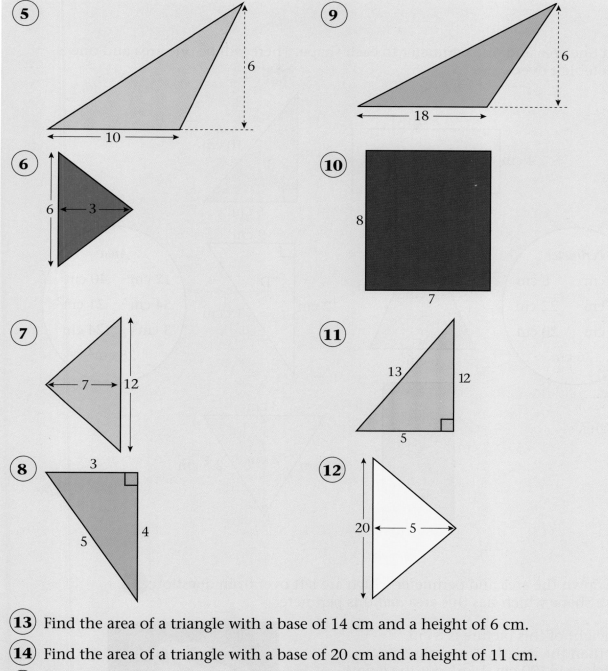

(5) 6, 10

(9) 6, 18

(6) 6, 3

(10) 8, 7

(7) 7, 12

(11) 13, 12, 5

(8) 3, 5, 4

(12) 20, 5

(13) Find the area of a triangle with a base of 14 cm and a height of 6 cm.

(14) Find the area of a triangle with a base of 20 cm and a height of 11 cm.

(15) A rectangle has an area of 80 cm². The width of the rectangle is 4 cm. What is the length of the rectangle?

(16) A triangle has an area of 40 cm². The base of the triangle is 16 cm. What is the height of the triangle?

?

area = 40 cm²

16 cm

E

1 Match one area and one perimeter to each shape. There will be one area and one perimeter left over.

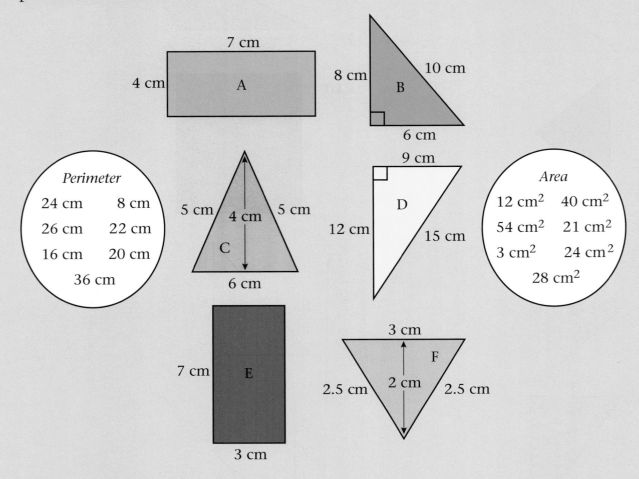

7 cm

4 cm — A

8 cm   10 cm   B   6 cm

Perimeter

24 cm	8 cm
26 cm	22 cm
16 cm	20 cm
36 cm	

5 cm   4 cm   5 cm   C   6 cm

9 cm   D   12 cm   15 cm

Area

12 cm²	40 cm²
54 cm²	21 cm²
3 cm²	24 cm²
28 cm²	

7 cm   E   3 cm

3 cm   F   2.5 cm   2 cm   2.5 cm

2 Write down the area and perimeter which are left over from question **1**. Draw a shape which has this area *and* this perimeter.

3 The height of this picture is 8 cm more than the length. The perimeter of the picture is 100 cm. Work out the length of the picture.

On these pages you will find areas of shapes made from rectangles and triangles.

Many shapes are made from rectangles and triangles.

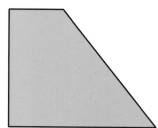

Can be cut
into a rectangle
and a triangle.

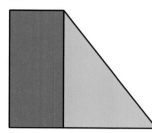

To find the area of the large shape, find the area of the rectangle and the area of the triangle then add them together.

Example

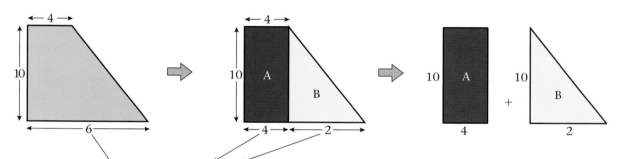

6 must equal 4 + 2 along the bottom side

Area rectangle A = 10 × 4 = 40

Area triangle B = $\frac{1}{2}$ × 2 × 10 = 10

Total area = 40 + 10 = 50

If each length is given in cm, the area of the shape is 50 cm².

Use triangles and rectangles to find the area of each shape in Questions ① to ⑫. All lengths are in cm.

①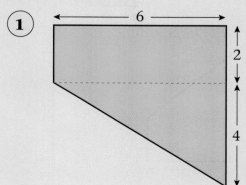

②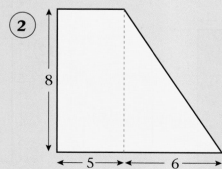

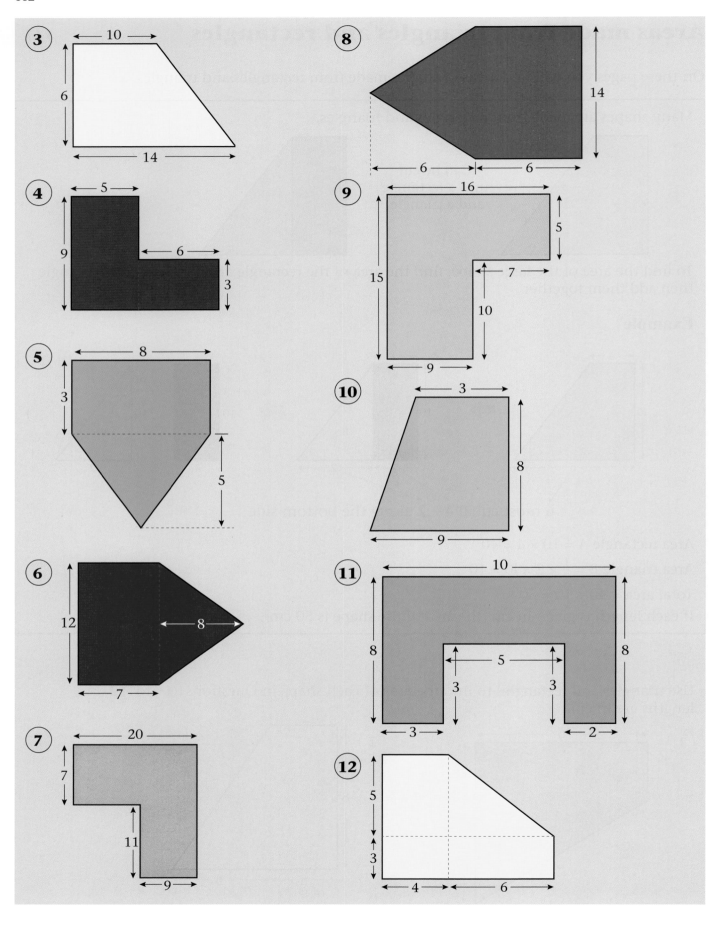

In each of Questions ⑬ to ⑯, find the shaded area.

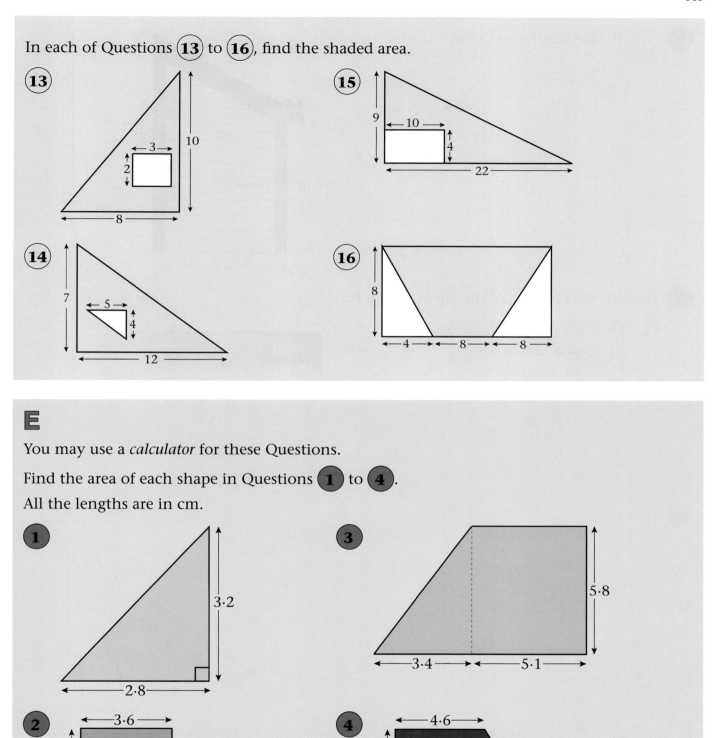

E

You may use a *calculator* for these Questions.

Find the area of each shape in Questions ① to ④.

All the lengths are in cm.

5 Find the area of the end of this shed.

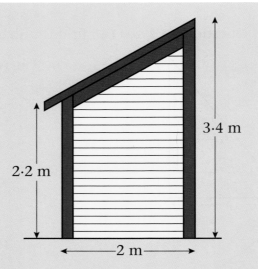

3·4 m

2·2 m

2 m

6 Find the area of each of the lawns shown below:

a)

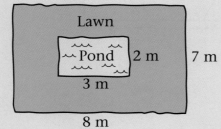

Lawn

Pond 2 m 7 m

3 m

8 m

b)

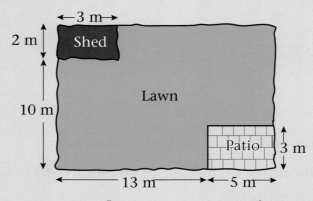

←3 m→

2 m Shed

10 m Lawn

Patio 3 m

13 m 5 m

7 Find the *total shaded area* in this shape.
All the lengths are in cm.

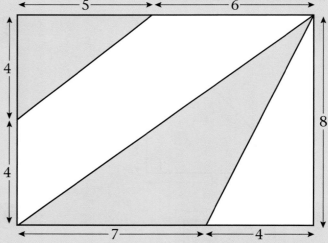

5 6

4

4

8

7 4

8 The area is written inside the triangle. Calculate *x*.

(a)

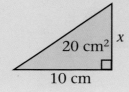

20 cm² x

10 cm

(b)

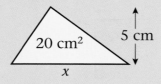

20 cm² 5 cm

x

On these pages you will find the surface area and volume of different cuboids.

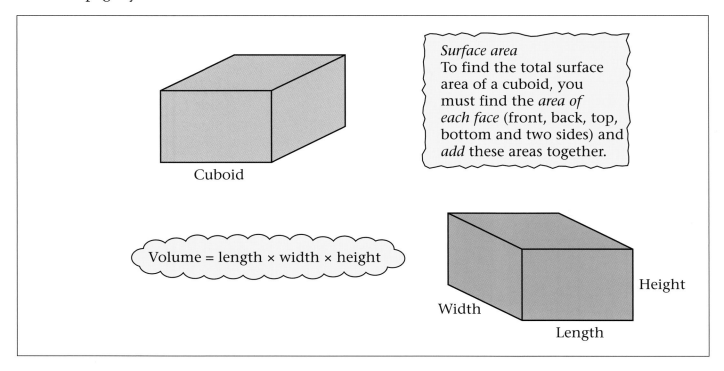

Cuboid

Surface area
To find the total surface area of a cuboid, you must find the *area of each face* (front, back, top, bottom and two sides) and *add* these areas together.

Volume = length × width × height

Width   Length   Height

1 Find the surface area of the top face of each cuboid:

(a) 3 cm   5 cm   4 cm

(b) 2 cm   10 cm   3 cm

(c) 8 cm   4 cm   6 cm

(d) 5 cm   20 cm   7 cm

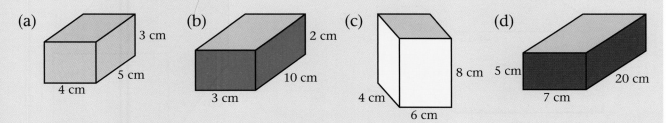

2 Find the surface area of the back face of each cuboid:

(a) 4 cm   8 cm   2 cm

(b) 6 cm   12 cm   5 cm

(c) 10 cm   3 cm   9 cm

(d) 6 cm   12 cm   2 cm

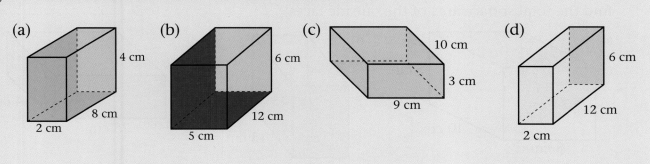

3 Copy and complete the tables below to find the *total surface area* of each cuboid.

a)

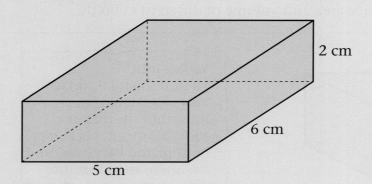

Face	Area (cm²)
Front	10
Back	
Top	
Bottom	
Side 1	
Side 2	12
	Total =

b)

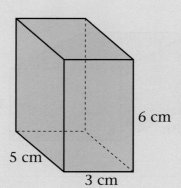

Face	Area (cm²)
Front	
Back	
Top	
Bottom	
Side 1	
Side 2	
	Total =

4 Find the *total surface area* of each cuboid below:

a)

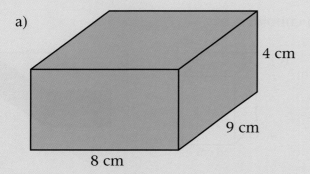

b)

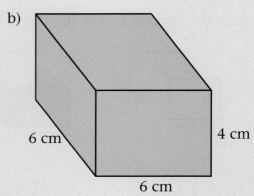

5 Each cuboid below is an open box (this means there is no top face). For each cuboid, find the total surface area of the outside faces.

a)

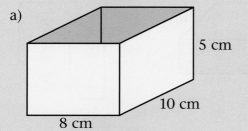

b)

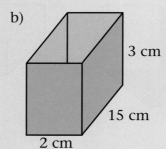

c)

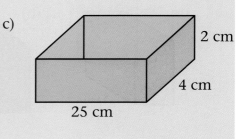

3

 E

Find the volume of each cuboid below:

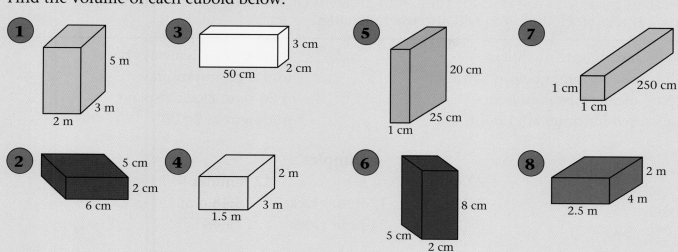

1 5 m, 3 m, 2 m

3 50 cm, 3 cm, 2 cm

5 20 cm, 25 cm, 1 cm

7 1 cm, 1 cm, 250 cm

2 5 cm, 2 cm, 6 cm

4 2 m, 3 m, 1.5 m

6 8 cm, 5 cm, 2 cm

8 2 m, 4 m, 2.5 m

Find the total surface area *and* the volume of each cuboid below:

9 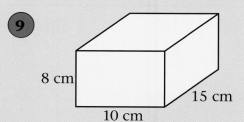 a pat of butter 10 cm × 15 cm × 8 cm

8 cm, 15 cm, 10 cm

10 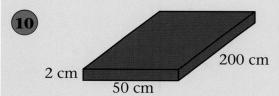 a plank of wood 50 cm × 200 cm × 2 cm

200 cm, 2 cm, 50 cm

11 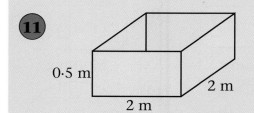 a paddling pool (no top face) 2 m × 2 m × 0.5 m

0·5 m, 2 m, 2 m

12 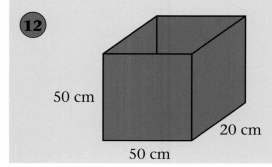 an open box 50 cm × 50 cm × 20 cm

50 cm, 20 cm, 50 cm

On these pages you will read the time from different clocks using 12-hour clock time and 24-hour clock time. You will also use timetables.

---

a.m. means ante meridiem.
It is used for times before noon.
p.m. means post meridiem.
It is used for times after noon.

24-hour clocks always have
four digits on display,
A 24-hour clock displays
midnight as 00:00

Examples

22 minutes past 8		12 minutes to 7
8:22 a.m.	12-hour clock	6:48 p.m.
08:22	24-hour clock	18:48

Morning

Evening

Ⓜ

Write each time shown to the nearest minute:

a) in words   b) in 12-hour clock time using a.m. and p.m..

①

Afternoon

②

Morning

③

Night

④

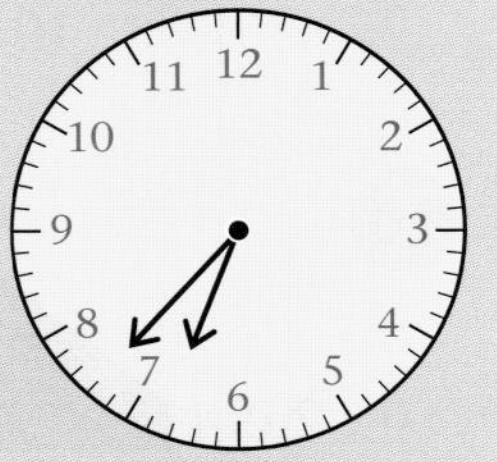

Evening

⑤ $\boxed{12:03}$

Lunchtime

⑥ $\boxed{4:49}$

Night

⑦ $\boxed{7:12}$

Evening

⑧ $\boxed{5:58}$

Morning

⑨

Afternoon

⑩

Night

⑪

Morning

⑫

Breakfast

⑬ Write the 12-hour clock times if each of the twelve clocks above was:

a) 9 minutes slow   b) 6 minutes fast.

14 Copy and complete the table.

TIME IN WORDS	12-HOUR CLOCK	24-HOUR CLOCK
three o' clock	3:00 p.m.	15:00
		07:45
		20:30
		10:35
		03:52
	10:19 p.m.	
	9:37a.m.	
	6:16 p.m.	
	11:28 a.m.	
	5:53 p.m.	

15 For each of the times in Question **14**, work out how many minutes there are to the next hour.

16 Look at the calendar.
Is this a leap year? How do you know?

FEBRUARY						
Su	M	Tu	W	Th	F	Sa
	1	2	3	4	5	6
7	8	9	10	11	12	13
14	15	16	17	18	19	20
21	22	23	24	25	26	27
28						

17 On what day will these children have their birthday?

a) Gavin — 4th February

b) Kate — 23rd February

c) Davina — 6th March

d) Amanda — 31st January

18 Christmas Day is a Tuesday.
What day of the week is New Year's Eve?

19 A school begins its half term holiday on Friday 23rd October. The holiday lasts one week. What is the date of the first Monday back at school?

20 It is June 15th. Levi's birthday is in three weeks time. What is the date of his birthday?

E

Use this train timetable for the questions below:

Waterloo (London)	07:10	08:35	11:35	13:50
Woking	07:35	–	12:00	14:15
Basingstoke	07:55	09:21	12:21	–
Andover	08:16	–	12:42	–
Salisbury	08:36	09:54	13:17	15:08
Yeovil	09:24	10:42	14:07	15:48
Honiton	10:01	–	14:53	16:34
Exeter	10:27	11:42	15:18	16:59

1 How long does it take the 07:10 from Waterloo to travel to:

   a) Woking   c) Andover?

   b) Basingstoke

2 At how many stations does the 11:35 from Waterloo stop?

3 At what time does the 08:35 from Waterloo reach Salisbury?

4 If you had to be in Exeter by 15:30 which train would you catch from Waterloo?

5 You arrive at Waterloo at 08:20. How long do you have to wait for the next train to Exeter?

6 The 11:35 from Waterloo runs 10 minutes late. At what time will it reach Andover?

7 How long does it take the 11:35 from Waterloo to travel to:

   a) Salisbury   c) Exeter?

   b) Yeovil

8 At how many stations does the 08:16 from Andover stop before it reaches Honiton?

9 At what time does the 12:21 from Basingstoke reach Yeovil?

10 If you had to be in Exeter by 12:00 which train would you catch from Basingstoke?

11 You arrive at Waterloo at 11:08. How long do you have to wait for the next train to Exeter?

12 The 08:35 from Waterloo runs 19 minutes late. At what time will it reach Exeter?

13 How long does it take the 07:55 from Basingstoke to travel to:

   a) Salisbury   c) Exeter?

   b) Yeovil

14 At how many stations does the 09:21 from Basingstoke stop before it reaches Exeter?

15 At what time does the 14:15 from Woking reach Honiton?

16 If you had to be in Honiton by 16:00 which train would you catch from Salisbury?

17 You arrive at Waterloo at 10:42. How long do you have to wait for the next train to Exeter?

18 The 11:35 from Waterloo runs 38 minutes late. At what time will it reach Honiton?

Estimation

On these pages you will round off numbers and work out rough answers for different problems.

- Using a calculator, √11 = 3.3166248

We can *round off* this number to either 1 or 2 decimal places.

- Rounding to one decimal place.

  If the figure in the 2nd decimal

  place is *5 or more*, round up.

  Otherwise do not.

  2.761 = 2.8 to 1 d.p.
  ↑

  13.45 = 13.5 to 1 d.p.
  ↑

  0.337 = 0.3 to 1 d.p.
  ↑

- Rounding to two decimal places.

  If the figure in the 3rd decimal

  place is *5 or more*, round up.

  Otherwise do not.

  1.4281 = 1.43 to 2 d.p.
  ↑

  0.0742 = 0.07 to 2 d.p.
  ↑

  8.555 = 8.56 to 2 d.p.
  ↑

Ⓜ **Part One**

① Round off these numbers correct to one decimal place.

a) 8.24   c) 0.762   e) 0.352   g) 11.518

b) 7.166   d) 11.27   f) 8.741   h) 0.648

② Round off these numbers correct to two decimal places.

a) 1.246   c) 11.222   e) 0.1355   g) 0.8592

b) 8.043   d) 3.084   f) 22.456   h) 6.097

③ Work out these answers on a calculator and then round off the answers correct to two decimal places.

a) 11.21 ÷ 7   d) 12.6 × 0.071   g) 1.36^2 j) 11.82 ÷ 13

b) 0.54 × 8.1   e) √13   h) 0.97^2 k) 2.4 × 0.716

c) 4216 ÷ 214   f) √8.5   i) 0.77 × 0.78   l) √(4.2 × 3.5)

④ Round off these numbers to the nearest hundred.

a) 1741   c) 807.1   e) 562.8   g) 3552

b) 22 483   d) 15 255   f) 2222   h) 1027

Ⓜ **Part Two**

① Estimate the lengths shown. Use the ruler as a guide

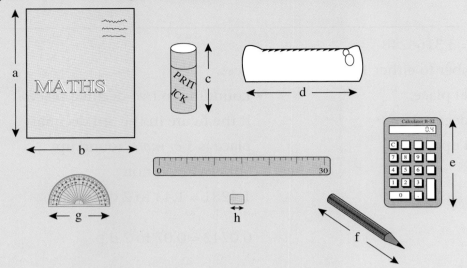

② Look at the picture. The person is about 2 metres tall.

Estimate the height of:

   a) The top of the roof of the house

   b) The ladder

   c) The tree

   d) The telegraph pole

   e) The nest box on the tree.

③ Estimate the reading on each thermometer.

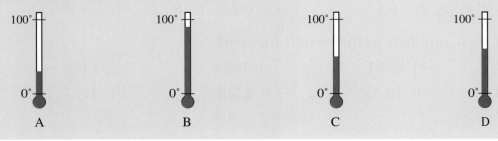

- Harry worked out 506.3 ÷ 9·5 and wrote down 5.3295.
  He can check his answer by working with estimates.
  Instead of 506.3 use 500, instead of 9.5 use 10.

  So 500 ÷ 10 = 50.

  Clearly Harry's answer is wrong. He put the decimal point in the wrong place.

- Here are three more calculations with estimates.

  a) 31.2 × 9.2

     ≈ 30 × 10

     ≈ 300

  b) 28.4 ÷ 0.971

     ≈ 30 ÷ 1

     ≈ 30

  c) 11% of £78.99

     ≈ $\frac{1}{10}$ of £80

     ≈ £8

E

Do not use a calculator.

From the table below, choose the most sensible ROUGH answer from A, B or C.

Calculation	A	B	C
1 6.73 × 9.65	30	70	300
2 2.3 × 96	200	90	20
3 1.02 × 60.7	6	60	200
4 5.14 × 5.99	15	10	30
5 18.8 × 20.7	200	400	4000
6 807 × 11.31	8000	4000	800
7 1.09 × 29.6	20	30	60
8 402 ÷ 4.97	8	0.8	80
9 601 ÷ 3.92	50	100	150
10 58.4 ÷ 0.98	60	300	600
11 217 ÷ 201.4	0.2	1	10
12 99 × 98	1 million	100 000	10 000
13 88.4 + 95 + 141	300	100	3000
14 0.32 + 0.294	0.06	0.1	0.6
15 11% of £198.20	£10	£20	£200

124

Do not use a calculator in Questions **16** to **20**.

16 A cut-price DVD was sold at £6.95 per copy. *Estimate* the total cost of 42 copies.

17 A do-it-yourself table and chairs kit cost £38.49.
Estimate the total cost of 11 kits.

18 The rent for a flat is £95 per week. *Estimate* the total spent on rent in one year (52 weeks in 1 year).

19 A calculator costs £5.99. *Estimate* the total cost of 31 calculators.

20 38 people pay a total of £1247 for a holiday trip. *Roughly how much* does each person pay?

Estimating game

- This is a game for two players. On squared paper draw an answer grid with the numbers shown.

Answer grid

198	1089	99	100	360	18
180	450	22	440	155	1980
1240	200	45	62	100	550
40	620	495	279	800	55
2000	80	220	10	891	250
4950	1550	1000	3960	3069	341

Question grid

2	5	9
11	20	31
40	50	99

The number obtained is crossed out on the answer grid using the player's own colour.

- The game continues until all the numbers in the answer grid have been crossed out. The object is to get four answers in a line (horizontally, vertically or diagonally). The winner is the player with most lines of four.

- A line of *five* counts as *two* lines of four. A line of *six* counts as *three* lines of four.

- The players now take turns to choose two numbers from the question grid below and multiply them on a calculator.

On this page you will practise adding and subtracting.

> **Remember**
> To add or subtract decimals, line up the decimal point.

Ⓜ

Work out (write out in columns first if you need to)

①
a) 17 + 23 + 56
b) 35 + 27 + 18
c) 16 + 39 + 17
d) 106 + 32 + 19
e) 159 + 216 + 17

f) 145 − 96
g) 221 − 108
h) 956 − 783
i) 902 − 583
j) 763 − 198

k) 19.6 + 3.2
l) 49.81 + 16.1
m) 16.02 + 7.5
n) 0.73 + 12.9
o) 3.77 + 21.08

②
a) 1937 + 213
b) 6541 + 2179
c) 1002 + 7466
d) 2983 + 6659
e) 3941 + 7988

f) 8193 − 218
g) 16527 − 4831
h) 17763 − 816
i) 25314 − 9368
j) 41835 − 9217

k) 368.2 − 195
l) 804 − 55.6
m) 39.45 − 17.1
n) 216.3 − 87.42
o) 531.2 − 104.56

③
a) £29.46 + £35.81 + £16.23
b) £103.90 + £78.57 + £19.02
c) £50.08 + £27.56 + £41.75
d) £38.57 + £19.92 + £28.07
e) £251.26 + £83.04 + £166.49

f) £19.08 − £6.43
g) £306.41 − £182.77
h) £93.02 − £57.64
i) £100 − £58.36
j) £253.71 − £189.94

Ⓔ

① Each member of a 4 × 100 m relay team ran their 100 m leg in 11.03, 10.95, 11.1 and 10.64. What was their total time?

② For 'Children in Need' Sachin, Paul and Leena raised £105.72, £98.46 and £138.10. How much did they raise altogether?

③ In a greyhound race the times for the first two dogs were 43.9 seconds and 44.06 seconds. How many seconds was the first dog quicker by?

④ The lengths of three worms were 10.53 cm, 9.6 cm and 8.69 cm. What was the total length of the three worms?

Ⓜ

Work out:

(1) 33 × 25   (6) 123 × 32   (11) 714 ÷ 17   (16) 864 ÷ 36

(2) 17 × 13   (7) 245 × 18   (12) 294 ÷ 14   (17) 609 ÷ 29

(3) 29 × 14   (8) 306 × 43   (13) 756 ÷ 12   (18) 612 ÷ 36

(4) 38 × 56   (9) 517 × 19   (14) 768 ÷ 32   (19) 990 ÷ 22

(5) 19 × 37   (10) 225 × 81   (15) 864 ÷ 16   (20) 361 ÷ 19

Ⓔ **Part One**

(1) 6 × 0.3   (6) 0.3 × 0.2   (11) 0.01 × 18   (16) 15.2 × 0.2

(2) 8 × 0.2   (7) 0.5 × 0.1   (12) 22 × 0.03   (17) 4.03 × 0.4

(3) 7 × 0.4   (8) 7 × 0.22   (13) 0.31 × 8   (18) 20.7 × 0.4

(4) 12 × 0.3   (9) 15 × 0.3   (14) 17 × 0.03   (19) 0.3^2

(5) 0.5 × 3   (10) 0.6 × 0.02   (15) 28 × 0.2   (20) 0.01^2

Dividing decimals by a whole number.

a) 8.76 ÷ 3

$$\begin{array}{r} 2.\ 92 \\ 3\overline{)8.^276} \end{array}$$

b) 25.48 ÷ 7

$$\begin{array}{r} 3.\ 6\ 4 \\ 7\overline{)25.^44^28} \end{array}$$

Part Two

Work out:

(1) 23.6 ÷ 4   (6) 22.4 ÷ 4   (11) Share £4.65 equally between five people

(2) 85.5 ÷ 5   (7) 2.36 ÷ 4

(3) 3.5 ÷ 7   (8) 8.55 ÷ 5

(4) 51 ÷ 3   (9) 0.35 ÷ 7

(5) 5.1 ÷ 3   (10) 2.24 ÷ 4

On these pages you will use a calculator to work out a mixture of number problems.

Copy the grid below.

Use a calculator to fill in the grid using the clues (IGNORE ANY DECIMAL POINTS).

¹		²	■	■	³	■
	■		■	⁴		■
■	■		■	⁵		⁶
■	⁷		⁸		■	
■		■		■	■	
⁹		¹⁰		■	¹¹	
	■		■	¹²		■

Clues across

1 2.5 + 3.1 × 2.4

4 90 ÷ 3 – 5 × 4

5 203 × 3 – (16 – 8)

7 2.5 × 1.67

9 131 × (32.71 + 17.29)

11 (72.8 – 32.8) × (1.67 + 0.33)

12 $\dfrac{(90 + 22.8)}{2.4}$

Clues down

1 (200 ÷ 4) + (40 + 2)

2 4081 – (2 × 40)

3 (167.2 + 232.8) × 2

4 2.6 – 1.9 × 0.5

6 (71 + 39) × (36 – 19)

7 2.5 × 1.7

8 (5 + 90) × (11 – 3)

9 $\dfrac{105.4}{1.7}$

10 (2053 – 92) ÷ (21.2 + 15.8)

11 (1.96 – 0.46) × 60 – 3

Copy the grid below.

Use a calculator to fill in the grid using the clues (IGNORE ANY DECIMAL POINTS).

Clues across

1 $\sqrt{289} + 11^2$

3 13% of 28

5 78% of 36

8 $9^2 - \sqrt{1}$

9 $\dfrac{(914 - 44)}{(7.2 + 2.8)}$

10 90% of 600

11 $\frac{3}{5}$ of 110

12 $\sqrt{6.25}$

14 $\sqrt{(181.6 - 70 + 9.4)}$

15 $(1063 + 1012) - (1.8 - 7.8)$

16 Change from £10 if you spend £3.94 (answer in pence only).

Clues down

1 $8^2 \times 27$

2 $9^2 \times (17 - 7)$

3 £1.28 – 89 pence (answer in pence only).

4 $\frac{5}{8}$ of 640

6 $(109.4 + 186.6)^2$

7 $\dfrac{17 \times 200}{40}$

8 $(7194 - 3180) \times (7 - 5)$

13 20% of 2550

15 $3^2 + 17$

On these pages you will investigate T-shapes on different sized grids.

T-shapes

1 Draw a grid as shown (your teacher may wish to give you a photocopied grid).

A large 'T' can be drawn inside the number square so that all 5 numbers in the T are inside the square.

1	2	3	4	5	6	7	8
9	10	11	12	13	14	15	16
17	18	19	20	21	22	23	24
25	26	27	28	29	30	31	32
33	34	35	36	37	38	39	40
41	42	43	44	45	46	47	48
49	50	51	52	53	54	55	56
57	58	59	60	61	62	63	64

The T can be moved around but it must stay upright.

1	2	3	4	5	6	7	8
9	10	11	12	13	14	15	16
17	18	19	20	21	22	23	24
25	26	27	28	29	30	31	32
33	34	35	36	37	38	39	40
41	42	43	44	45	46	47	48
49	50	51	52	53	54	55	56
57	58	59	60	61	62	63	64

The 'T' number is the first number in the top row.

We shall call the shape below T17 because the T-number is 17.

17	18	19
	26	
	34	

2 What is the smallest possible T-number?

3 Work out the total of the numbers in T21.

4 'Find a rule which connects the T-number with the total of all the numbers in a T-shape' (call this the T-total).

FOLLOW THESE STEPS:

a) Find the T-total for Tl (i.e. add up all the numbers in Tl.)

b) Find the T-total for T2.

c) Find the T-total for T3 then T4 then T5.

d) Write the answers in a table like below:

T-number n	T-total T
1	
2	
3	
4	
5	

e) Is there a pattern for the T-total numbers? They should increase by the same number each time.

f) There will be a two-stage rule which connects the T-number with the T-total as follows:

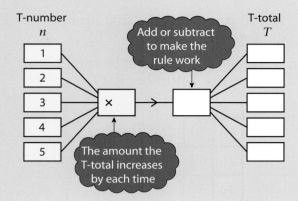

g) Can you write your rule as a formula?

(*Example*. If rule is

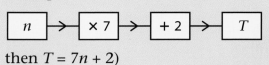

then $T = 7n + 2$)

5 It is *VERY IMPORTANT* to *CHECK* your rule. Look at the grid and find the T-total for T10. Use $n = 10$ in your formula. Do you get the same answer?

Look at the grid and find the T-total for T30. Use $n = 30$ in your formula. Do you get the same answer?

Hopefully everything works!

E

1 Draw a grid as shown (called a 7 × 7 grid)

(your teacher may wish to give you a photocopied grid).

1	2	3	4	5	6	7
8	9	10	11	12	13	14
15	16	17	18	19	20	21
22	23	24	25	26	27	28
29	30	31	32	33	34	35
36	37	38	39	40	41	42
43	44	45	46	47	48	49

2 Find a rule which connects the T-number with the T-total for any T-shape drawn in this new grid (i.e. FOLLOW THE SAME STEPS AS YOU DID FOR THE 8 × 8 GRID IN SECTION M).

3

1	2	3	4	5	6
7	8	9	10	11	12
13	14	15	16	17	18
19	20	21	22	23	24
25	26	27	28	29	30
31	32	33	34	35	36

Now do the same for a 6 × 6 grid, i.e. find a rule which connects the T-number with the T-total for any T-shape drawn in this new grid.

4 Do the same as above for as many different grids as you can.

5 For each different grid, write down your formula or rule.

> **Example**
>
> | | |
> |---|---|
> | 4 × 4 grid | $T = 8n + 11$ |
> | 5 × 5 grid | $T = 8n + 21$ |
> | 6 × 6 grid | $T = 8n + 31$ |
> | 7 × 7 grid | $T = 8n + 41$ |
> | 8 × 8 grid | $T = 8n + 51$ |

Look at YOUR formulas. Can you see any more patterns.

Write down anything you notice.

Discuss with your teacher.

Write down anything else about doing this problem that you feel is useful.

On these pages you will add, subtract, multiply and divide negative numbers.

Ⓜ

```
 -8 -7 -6 -5 -4 -3 -2 -1  0  1  2  3  4  5  6  7  8
◄──┼──┼──┼──┼──┼──┼──┼──┼──┼──┼──┼──┼──┼──┼──┼──┼──►
    F      D        A        G     B     C     E
```

① Put the following in order of size – smallest first:

a) B, D, A, G

b) A, D, F, B

c) 4, –6, –2, 8

d) 5, 10, –3, –9, 6

e) –6, –12, 10, 4, 8

f) 5, –2, 0, 4, 6

g) –12, 6, –9, 3, 18

h) 10, 2, –12, 4, –11

i) –8, –1, 2, –3, –5

j) –5, 4, –1, 3, 6

② What letter above is the answer to:

a) –4 – 3

b) –4 + 3

c) 4 – 5

d) –1 + 3

e) 2 – 6

f) 4 – 8

g) 8 – 15

h) –2 + 6

i) B – 5

j) E – 6

k) D + 6

l) G – 9

m) A – 6

n) G – 6

o) C + 2

p) D + 10

③ Copy and complete the boxes below:

```
-3 + 2 = -1
-3 + 5 = □
+4 - 2 = □
□ - 3 = -8
□ - 4 = -5
```

```
+6 - 3 = □
□ + 2 = -5
-8 - 6 = □
+4 - □ = -5
-7 + □ = +2
```

```
+12 - 6 = □
□ - 3 = -2
-8 + 2 = □
-5 + □ = 0
0 + 6 = □
```

Two signs together

Remember: it is possible to replace two signs next to each other by one sign as follows:

```
+  +  =  +
-  -  =  +
-  +  =  -
+  -  =  -
```

'same signs: +'

'different signs: –'

Examples

a) $5 - (-3) = 5 + 3 = 8$

b) $-6 + (-2) = -6 - 2 = -8$

Work out:

4 a) 5 – (+2)   e) –8 – (+2)   i) 10 – (–5)   m) 2 + (–3)

  b) 5 – (–2)   f) –8 – (–2)   j) 10 – (+5)   n) 2 – (–3)

  c) –3 + (+4)   g) 6 – (+3)   k) 7 – (+8)   o) 4 – (+6)

  d) –3 + (–4)   h) 6 – (–3)   l) 7 – (–8)   p) 4 – (–6)

5 Copy the following sequences and fill in the missing numbers:

  a) –5, –3, ☐, ☐, 3, 5   f) 1.2, 0.8, ☐, 0, ☐

  b) –12, ☐, –4, ☐, 4, 8   g) –3.6, –2.7, ☐, –0.9, ☐

  c) –8, –5, ☐, ☐, 4, 7   h) –50, ☐, 0, 25, ☐

  d) –10, ☐, –2, 2, 6, ☐   i) ☐, ☐, –1, 5, 11

  e) –20, –12, ☐, ☐, 12, 20   j) ☐, ☐, 1, 10, 19

Multiplying and dividing

  A   B   C   D

  ↓   ↓   In the sequence of multiplications   ↓   ↓   In this sequence

5 × 3 = 15   shown, the numbers in column A   –3 × 3 = –9   the numbers in

5 × 2 = 10   go down by one each time.   –3 × 2 = –6   column C go down

5 × 1 = 5   The numbers in column B   –3 × 1 = –3   by one each time.

5 × 0 = 5   go down by five each time.   –3 × 0 = 0

5 × –1 = –5   Continuing the sequence: –3 × –1 = 3   The numbers in

5 × –2 = –10   We see that: –3 × –2 = 6   column D *increase*

5 × –3 = –15   –3 × –3 = 9   by 3 each time.

We see that: We see that:

> When a positive number is multiplied by a negative number the answer is negative.

> When two negative numbers are multiplied together the answer is positive.

> For division, the rules are the same as for multiplication.

Examples

–3 × (–7) = 21   5 × (–3) = –15   –12 ÷ 3 = –4

20 ÷ (–2) = –10   –40 ÷ (–20) = 2   –1 × (–2) × (–3) = –6

E

Work out:

1 a) 2×5 b) $2 \times (-5)$ c) -2×5 d) $-2 \times (-5)$

2 a) 3×6 b) $3 \times (-6)$ c) -3×6 d) $-3 \times (-6)$

3 a) 12×4 b) $12 \times (-4)$ c) -12×4 d) $-12 \times (-4)$

4 a) 8×7 b) $8 \times (-7)$ c) -8×7 d) $-8 \times (-7)$

5 a) 4×9 b) $4 \times (-9)$ c) -4×9 d) $-4 \times (-9)$

6 a) $10 \div 2$ b) $10 \div (-2)$ c) $-10 \div (-2)$ d) $-10 \div 2$

7 a) $18 \div 3$ b) $18 \div (-3)$ c) $-18 \div (-3)$ d) $-18 \div 3$

8 a) $42 \div 7$ b) $42 \div (-7)$ c) $-42 \div (-7)$ d) $-42 \div 7$

9 a) $48 \div 12$ b) $48 \div (-12)$ c) $-48 \div (-12)$ d) $-48 \div 12$

10 a) $77 \div 11$ b) $77 \div (-11)$ c) $-77 \div (-11)$ d) $-77 \div 11$

11 Find the missing numbers:

a) $-4 \times \boxed{} = 12$ e) $\boxed{} \times (-3) = 9$ i) $-2 \times \boxed{} = 20$

b) $3 \times \boxed{} = -12$ f) $12 \div \boxed{} = -6$ j) $-3 \times \boxed{} = 6$

c) $-8 \div (-4) = \boxed{}$ g) $\boxed{} \div (-3) = 2$ k) $-2 \times \boxed{} = 4$

d) $5 \times \boxed{} = -5$ h) $\boxed{} \div 5 = -4$ l) $(-1)^2 = \boxed{}$

Factors, multiples and prime numbers

On this page you will find and use factors, multiples and prime numbers.

Remember:

Multiples are the numbers in a multiplication table.

8, 16, 24, 32, 40, . . . are multiples of 8.

A *factor* is a number which divides exactly into another number (there will be no remainder).

The factors of 10 are 1, 2, 5, 10.

A *prime* number can only be divided by two different numbers (these are the number 1 and itself).

The first three prime numbers are 2, 3 and 5.

M

(1) Write down the first 5 multiples of:

    a) 2   b) 6   c) 4   d) 7   e) 9

(2) a) Write down the first 6 multiples of both 3 and 5. What is the lowest number in both lists?

    Do the same for   b) 5 and 6   c) 4 and 5

(3) From these lists pick out the multiples of the number in the brackets:

    a) 2 3 5 7   10 12   (3)

    b) 4 6 8 10   11 15   (4)

    c) 3 5 7 9   11 15   (5)

    d) 2 4 6 8   10 12   (6)

(4) Write down all the prime numbers shown in Question **(3)**.

E

(1) Write down *all* the factors of the following numbers:

    a) 12   c) 24   e) 20   g) 22

    b) 18   d) 32   f) 30   h) 33

(2) Write down the next prime number after:

    a) 30   b) 37   c) 50   d) 24

(3) Which of these numbers are multiples of 6:

    a) 36   b) 64   c) 48   d) 666

On these pages you will find square numbers, cube numbers and square roots.

Remember:

When a number is multiplied by itself you get a *square number*.

$5^2 = 5 \times 5 = 25$ (we say '5 squared is 25')

The *square root* of 25 is 5 because 5 multiplied by itself is 25.

$\sqrt{25} = 5$ (we say 'the square root of 25 is 5')

M

1) Work out:

a) 8×8 c) 2×2 e) 10×10 g) 4^2 i) 5^2

b) 7×7 d) 9×9 f) 3^2 h) 10^2 j) 6^2

2) Copy and complete the following:

a) If $11 \times 11 = 121$, the square root of $121 = \Box$

b) If $13 \times 13 = 169$, the square root of $169 = \Box$

c) If $14 \times 14 = 196$, the square root of $196 = \Box$

d) If $15 \times 15 = 225$, then $\sqrt{225} = \Box$

e) If $16 \times 16 = 256$, then $\sqrt{256} = \Box$

3) Work out:

a) $\sqrt{64}$ b) $\sqrt{36}$ c) $\sqrt{81}$ d) $\sqrt{49}$ e) $\sqrt{100}$

4) Copy and complete the following by filling in the boxes:

a) $3^2 = \Box$ e) $3^{\Box} = 9$ i) $\sqrt{36} = \Box$

b) $\Box^2 = 64$ f) $49 = \Box^2$ j) $\sqrt{\Box} = 8$

c) $\Box^2 = 81$ g) $\sqrt{9} = \Box$ k) $\sqrt{\Box} = 9$

d) $5^2 = \Box$ h) $\sqrt{100} = \Box$ l) $\sqrt{\Box} = 1$

Remember:

2^3 means $2 \times 2 \times 2 = 4 \times 2 = 8$

We say '2 cubed = 8'

4^3 means $4 \times 4 \times 4 = 16 \times 4 = 64$

E

1 Write each Question in the 'shorter' way as shown in part (a):

a) $5 \times 5 \times 5 = \boxed{5^3}$

b) $6 \times 6 \times 6 = \boxed{}$

c) $8 \times 8 \times 8 = \boxed{}$

d) $3 \times 3 \times 3 = \boxed{}$

e) $7 \times 7 \times 7 = \boxed{}$

f) $12 \times 12 \times 12 = \boxed{}$

g) $9 \times 9 \times 9 = \boxed{}$

h) $11 \times 11 \times 11 = \boxed{}$

2 Copy and complete the following. Part a) has been done for you.

a) 5^3 means $\boxed{5 \times 5 \times 5}$

b) 7^3 means $\boxed{}$

c) 8^3 means $\boxed{}$

d) 6^2 means $\boxed{}$ (Be careful!)

e) 3^3 means $\boxed{}$

f) 8^2 means $\boxed{}$

3 Work out:

a) $2 \times 2 \times 2$

b) $5 \times 5 \times 5$

c) $4 \times 4 \times 4$

d) $3 \times 3 \times 3$

e) 6^3

f) 10^3

g) 7^3

h) 9^3

4 Use your answers for Question **3** to complete:

a) $2^3 = \boxed{}$

b) $10^3 = \boxed{}$

c) $\boxed{}^3 = 27$

d) $4^{\boxed{}} = 64$

e) 5 cubed $= \boxed{}$

f) 7 cubed $= \boxed{}$

5 Work out:

a) $3^2 + 2^3$

b) $4^2 - 1^3$

c) $4^3 + \sqrt{100}$

d) $2^1 + 2^2 + 2^3$

1. Draw a grid on squared paper like this.

   Label across from 0 to 15 (horizontal axis).

   Label up from 0 to 20 (vertical axis).

   Plot the points below and join them up with a ruler in the order given.

(11, 10)	(5, 7)	(6, 7)	(6, 7½)
(7, 7½)	(7, 8)	(10, 4)	(13, 6)
(14, 5)	(12, 2)	(10, 4)	(8, 2)
(9, 5)			

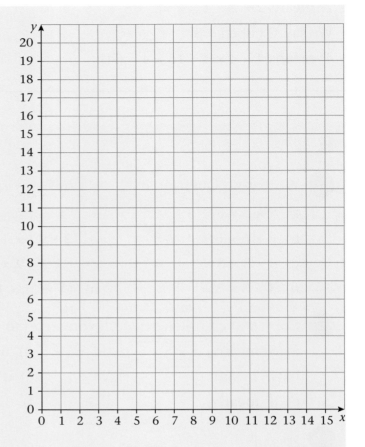

On the same picture, plot the points below and join them up with a ruler in the order given. *Do not* join the last point in the box above with the first point in the new box.

> (8, 11) (10, 11)

On the same picture, plot the points below and join them up in order.

> (15, 16) (13½, 16) (14½, 14) (14, 13) (12, 16) (12, 18) (11, 20)

On the same picture, plot the points below and join them up in order.

> (14, 17) (12, 19)   then   (14, 18) (13, 19)

On the same picture, plot the points below and join them up in order.

> (9, 0) (9½, 2) (9, 3) (9½, 2) (10½, 2) (11, 3) (10½, 2) (11, 0)

On the same picture, plot the points below and join them up in order.

> (4, 11) (4, 14) (4, 12½) (5½, 12½)   then   (5, 7) (4, 7) (4, 8½)

On the same picture, plot the points below and join them up in order.

(7, 13) (9, 13) (11, 14) (11, 13) (10, 12) (8, 12) (7, 13)

On the same picture, plot the points below and join them up in order.

(13, 6) (13, 10) (15, 14) (15, 18) (14, 20) (9, 20) (5, 18) (4, 17)
(4, 14) (6, 13) $(1\frac{1}{2}, 8\frac{1}{2})$ (1, 7) (5, 9) (5, 10) (4, 10)

On the same picture, plot the points below and join them up in order.

(7, 8) (8, 8) $(8, 8\frac{1}{2})$ $(9, 8\frac{1}{2})$ (9, 9) (10, 9) $(10, 9\frac{1}{2})$

Draw a ⊗ at (10, 18) and a ⊗ at (10, 19) and another ⊗ at (11, 18)

Draw a • at (5, 13) and a • at (10, 13)

Who am I? Colour me in.

(**2**) Copy this grid.

Label across from –3 to 9 (horizontal axis).

Label up from –4 to 13 (vertical axis).

Plot the points below and join them up with a ruler in the order given.

(4, 8) (6, 8) (6, 5) (1, 5) (1, 8)
(4, 8) (4, 4) (2, 4) (2, 6) (4, 6)

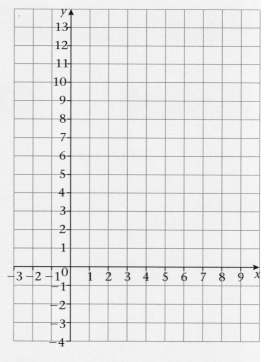

On the same picture plot the points below and join them up with a ruler in the order given.

Do not join the last point in the box above with the first point in the new box.

(–2, 4) (–2, 1) (–1, –1) (5, –1) (4, –3) (–2, –3) (–1, –1)

On the same picture, plot the points below and join them up in order.

(0, 1)   (1, –1)   then   (1, 1)   (2, –1)   then   (1, 9)   (2, 9)

On the same picture, plot the points below and join them up in order.

(1, 10)   (2, 10)   then   (l, 11)   (2, 11)   then   (–1, 4)   (–2, 5)

On the same picture, plot the points below and join them up in order.

(4, –1)   (3, 1)   (4, 2)   (7, 2) $(8\frac{1}{2}, 1)$ (4, 1) $(4, 1\frac{1}{2})$ $(4, \frac{1}{2})$

On the same picture, plot the points below and join them up in order.

(–1, 3)   (–3, 5)   (–3, 6)   (–2, 6)   then   (6, –3)   (5, –1)   (7, 1)

On the same picture, plot the points below and join them up in order.

(7, 2)   (7, 3)   (5, 5)   (5, 4) $(6\frac{1}{2}, 4)$ $(6\frac{1}{2}, 6)$ (5, 6)   (5, 5)

On the same picture, plot the points below and join them up in order.

(5, 8)   (2, 12)   (–1, 12)   (–2, 11)   (–2, 6) $(-\frac{1}{2}, 5)$ (2, 6)

On the same picture, plot the points below and join them up in order.

(–2, 8)   (–1, 8)   then   (–2, 9)   (–1, 9)   then   (–2, 10)   (–1, 10)

then   (–2, 11)   (–1, 11)

Draw a • at (2,   7) and a • at (5,   7)

Who am I? Colour me in.

Probability

On these pages you will work out the chance of certain events happening, sometimes by listing all the possible outcomes.

Remember:

$$\text{Expected probability} = \frac{\text{the number of ways the event can happen}}{\text{the number of possible outcomes}}$$

Example

10 identical discs numbered 1, 2, 3, 4, 5, 6, 7, 8, 9, 10 are put into a bag.
One disc is selected at random.

There are 10 possible outcomes.

(a)   The probability of selecting a '2' = $\frac{1}{10}$

     This may be written p (selecting a '2') = $\frac{1}{10}$

(b)   p (*not* selecting a 2) = $\frac{9}{10}$ (Note $\frac{9}{10} = 1 - \frac{1}{10}$)

(c)   p (selecting a number greater than 7) = $\frac{3}{10}$

(d)   p (*not* selecting a number greater than 7) = $\frac{7}{10}$ (*Note* $\frac{7}{10} = 1 - \frac{3}{10}$)

Learn

If the probability of an event occurring is p, then the probability of it *not* occurring is 1–p.

---

1   Ten discs numbered 1, 3, 3, 3, 4, 7, 8, 9, 11, 11 are placed in a bag. One disc is selected at random. Find the probability that it is:

    (a)   a three   (b)   an even number   (c)   less than 6

2   10 balls numbered 2, 2, 2, 7, 7, 7, 7, 7, 9, 9 are put into a box. One ball is chosen at random. Find the probability of:

    (a)   choosing a '2'   (b)   *not* choosing a '9'   (c)   *not* choosing a '7'

3   11 discs are put into a bag. Four discs are red, the rest of the discs are blue. One disc is selected at random. Find the probability that it is:

    (a)   red   (b)   *not* blue   (c)   *not* red

4 A bag contains nine balls: three red, four white and two yellow.

(a) Find the probability of selecting a red ball.

(b) The two yellow balls are *replaced* by two white balls.
Find the probability of *not* selecting a white ball.

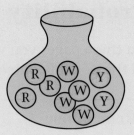

5

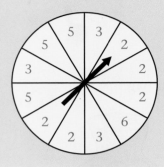

A spinner has twelve equal sectors as shown.
Find the probability of:

(a) spinning a '6'

(b) spinning a '2'

(c) *not* spinning a '5'

(d) *not* spinning an even number

(e) *not* spinning a prime number.

When two events can happen, it is often helpful to make a list of all the possible outcomes.
It is *important* to *use a system*.

Example

Throwing 2 coins.

Using H for 'head' and T for 'tail', two coins can land as:

1st coin	2nd coin
H	H
H	T
T	H
T	T

E

 A coin and a dice are tossed together.

(a) List all the possible outcomes in a table:

coin	dice

(b) What is the probability of getting a head on the coin and a 6 on the dice?

2 For lunch, Rory eats soup or a sandwich. He drinks water or lemonade. Copy and complete the table below to show all the different lunches he might have.

food	drink
soup	water
soup	

3 Four friends, Jen, Ken, Len and Mick, each write their name on a card and the four cards are placed in a hat. Two cards are chosen to decide who does the washing-up that day.

(a) List all the possible pairs of names.

(b) What is the probability that Ken and Len are chosen?

4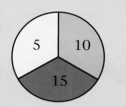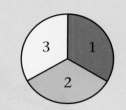
Kay has these two spinners. She spins both spinners and adds up the numbers to get a total. For example a '10' and a '2' give a total of 12.

(a) Make a list of all the possible totals. Use the table shown to help.

1st spinner	2nd spinner	Total
5	1	6
5		

(b) What is the probability of getting a total of 8?

5 Three coins are tossed together. List all the possible outcomes for the three coins (there are *eight* possible outcomes).

What is the probability of tossing three heads?

On these pages you should consider probabilities to work out the winner of a race.

AN HOUR AT THE RACES!

This task is more fun done as a whole class with the teacher but could be done in smaller groups.

You are going to bet on a horse race.

Each person has £100 to start with. You may choose no more than two horses to win. If your horse wins, you will win back double the money you bet on that horse.

(1) Firstly the teacher must tell you how many races there will be.

(2) Each race will have eleven horses. Make up eleven names. Number each horse from 2 up to 12.

(3) On the board or on paper, draw the racetrack with ten squares as shown below:

Start (name)											Finish
2 Smart dog											
3 Tornado											
4											

(4) The race is run by throwing two dice and adding up the total score. This score tells you which horse may move forward 1 square. So if you throw a '1 and a '2', the score is 3 and Tornado moves forward 1 square. (Put a cross in the next square for this horse). The winner is the first horse to move into the 'Finish' box.

(5) Bet on two horses to win.

(6) Start throwing the dice and enjoy the race!

(7) Who won? How much money have you got left? *Discuss* with your teacher which horses have the best chance of winning and why that is.

(a) What is the probability of horse 7 winning?

(b) What is the probability of horse 4 winning?

(c) What is the probability of horse 12 winning?

8 Have a new race. Bet on two horses to win (if you have any money left!) Are you using probability to help or are you just a pointless gambler?

9 Run the race. Sort out the money.

Will working out the best probability of winning always ensure you win the bet *everytime* you have a race like this? *Discuss* with your teacher.

E

It is harder for some horses to win than others in this game. Your teacher may wish to place 'odds' on each horse to win. For example, if horse 2 wins, you get 20 times your bet back.

Sort out the 'odds' then run some more races. *Discuss* with your teacher whether gambling is a very good idea!

On these pages you will look at whether shapes have reflective symmetry or rotational symmetry.

Remember:

A shape is symmetrical if half its shape matches the other half exactly.

The line separating the two halves is the line of symmetry or mirror line.

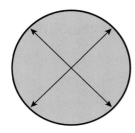

This shape fits onto itself four times when rotated through a complete turn.

It has *rotational symmetry of order 4*.

M

(1) How many lines of symmetry (if any) do the shapes and letters below have?

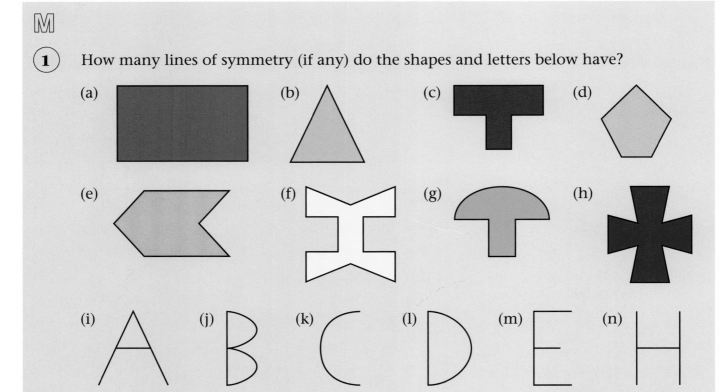

(a)   (b)   (c)   (d)

(e)   (f)   (g)   (h)

(i) A   (j) B   (k) C   (l) D   (m) E   (n) H

(2) *If* your teacher wants you to, copy each shape and letter above and draw all the lines of symmetry.

Scale Drawings

On these pages you will make scale drawings.

A rectangle has length 30 m and width 20 m.

Draw an accurate scale drawing of the rectangle using a scale of 1 cm for every 5 m.

Length 30 m will be 30 ÷ 5 = 6 cm on the drawing.

Width 20 m will be 20 ÷ 5 = 4 cm on the drawing.

Scale drawing:

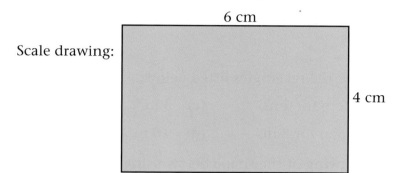

Ⓜ

Draw an accurate scale drawing of each shape below using the scale shown.

①

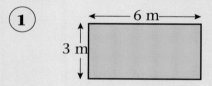

Scale: 1 cm for every 3 m

③

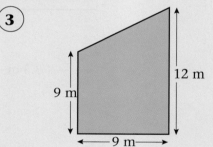

Scale: 1 cm for every 3 m

②

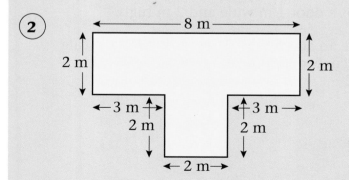

Scale: 1 cm for every 2 m

④

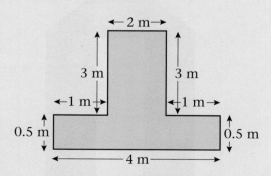

Scale: 1 cm for every 0·5 m

5

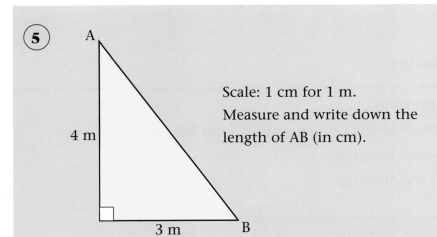

Scale: 1 cm for 1 m.
Measure and write down the
length of AB (in cm).

6 Use the given scale to draw the rectangles listed below:

(a) 5 m × 10 m   Scale: 1 cm for 5 m.

(b) 12 m × 8 m   Scale: 1 cm for 2 m.

(c) 3 m × 15 m   Scale: 1 cm for 3 m.

(d) 10 m × 15 m   Scale: 1 cm for 5 m.

7 Make an accurate scale drawing of the shape below using a scale of 2 cm for every 1 m.

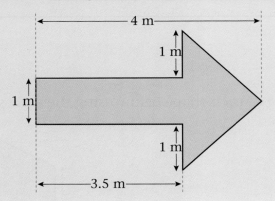

E

1

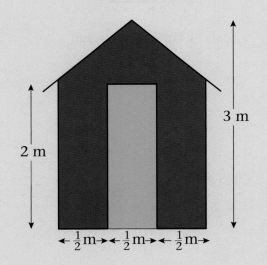

A sentry box is 3 m high and $1\frac{1}{2}$ m wide.

It has a door $\frac{1}{2}$ m wide and 2 m high.

Make an accurate scale drawing using a scale
of 2 cm for every 1 m.

This is a plan of Mr. Cooper's house and gardens. It has been drawn to a scale of 1 cm for every 2 m.

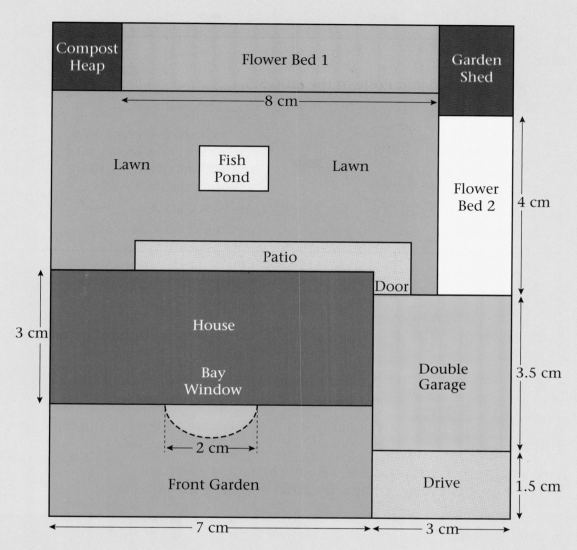

2 How wide is:

   (a) the front garden   (b) the drive   (c) the bay window?

3 How long is flower bed 2?

4 How wide is flower bed 1?

5 If the fish pond is 4 m wide, what size should it be on the plan?

6 Measure carefully the width of the patio on the plan. How many *metres* wide is the real patio?

7 What is the real *area* of the double garage?

On these pages you will solve problems using ratios.

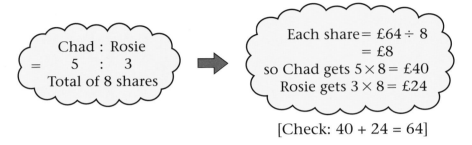

Reminder.

Divide £64 between Chad and Rosie in the ratio 5:3.

Chad : Rosie
= 5 : 3
Total of 8 shares

Each share = £64 ÷ 8
= £8
so Chad gets 5 × 8 = £40
Rosie gets 3 × 8 = £24

[Check: 40 + 24 = 64]

(1) Ranjit and Darvinder share the cost of a present for their sister in the ratio 5:4. If the present cost £27, how much was Ranjit's share?

(2) A baker makes white bread, brown bread and wholemeal bread in the ratio 5:4:1. If he makes 80 brown loaves, how many white loaves does he make?

(3) In class 9F the ratio of boys to girls is 5:7. If there are 15 boys in the class, how many girls are there?

(4) The weights of 3 Sumo-wrestlers are in the ratio 4:5:6. If the heaviest weighs 120 kg, what is the total weight of the other two?

(5) The girls at a local school choose Rugby, Soccer and Skiing in the ratio 3:5:4. If 20 choose Skiing, how many choose Soccer? How many girls are there altogether?

(6) A sum of money is shared in the ratio 2:3:4. If the smaller share is 30 p, what are the other two shares?

(7) John is 5 years old and Helen is 7 years old. They share a prize in the ratio of their ages. If Helen gets £21, how much does John get?

(8) A dog and its pup eat food in the ratio 3:1. If the dog eats 90 grams of meat, how much will the pup eat?

(9) A farmer has cows, sheep and pigs in the ratio 3:5:7. If there are 49 pigs, how many cows are there?

E

1 Michael has four stamps for every three Sandra has. Michael has 600 stamps. How many stamps does Sandra have?

2 In a class of 30 there are two fair-haired children to every three with darker hair. How many children have fair hair?

3 There are 60 apples in a box. Two in every five apples are red. The rest are green. How many green apples are there?

4 Bradley has six times as many conkers as Sandeep. Sandeep has 8 conkers. How many does Bradley have?

5 During the season the school football team scored five goals to every four scored by their opponents. 63 goals were scored in the matches. How many goals were scored by the school team?

6 There were 40 passengers on a bus. Three in every eight sat upstairs. How many passengers sat downstairs?

7 A shop sells 8 times as many white shirts as black shirts. 72 white shirts are sold. How many black shirts are sold?

8 A farmer has 5 sheep for every 2 cows.

He has 300 sheep. How many cows does he have?

9 Reduce these ratios to their simplest form (remember: the *units* must be made the *same* first).

(a)   60 p : £1

(d)   £2.50 : £3.50

(g)   700 kg : 1 tonne

(b)   150 cm : 2 m

(e)   50 cm : 1 m

(h)   20 mm : 3 cm

(c)   750 g : 1 kg

(f)   400 ml : 2 litres

(i)   60 cm : 2 m

10 You can make different colours of paint by mixing red, blue and yellow in different proportions.

(a)   To make purple, you mix 4 parts red to 6 parts blue. How much of each colour do you need to make 20 litres of purple paint?

(b)   To make orange, you mix 12 parts yellow to 8 parts red. How much of each colour do you need to make 10 litres of orange paint?

11 A cake contains flour, sugar and butter in the ratio 15:7:3. The total amount of flour, sugar and butter used is 1 kg (1000 g).

(a)   How many grams of butter are used?

(b)   How many grams of sugar are used?

(c)   How many grams of flour are used?

12 In August, a family spends money on heating, food and travel in the ratio 2:5:8. In total, the family spent £450. How much was spent on travel?

Puzzle Page – Operator Squares

Each empty square contains either a number or an operation (+, −, ×, ÷).
Copy each square and fill in the missing details. The arrows are equals signs.

1

15	÷	3	→	
+		×		
		5	→	110
↓		↓		
37	−		→	

2

14	+		→	31
×		+		
4		23	→	92
↓		↓		
	−		→	

3

	×	5	→	40
+		−		
	×	2	→	
↓		↓		
19	×		→	

4

8	×	20	→	
÷		÷		
	×	5	→	
↓		↓		
4	×		→	

5

	×	5	→	105
−		×		
9	×	6	→	
↓		↓		
	×		→	

6

	+	5	→	6.2
×		+		
10		2.4	→	24
↓		↓		
	−		→	4.6

7

2	×	60	→	
+		÷		
10	÷		→	2
↓		↓		
	×		→	

8

18	×	6	→	
÷		÷		
9	×	12	→	
↓		↓		
	×		→	

9

38	×	8	→	
÷		×		
2	×		→	
↓		↓		
	+	112	→	

10

	×	5	→	120
÷		×		
	−	8	→	0
↓		↓		
	×		→	

11

8.42	−	0.2	→	
×		×		
100	×		→	1200
↓		↓		
	+		→	

12

	×	(−4)	→	−12
÷		+		
	−		→	
↓		↓		
−1	+	−3	→	

Revision 1 – Place Value, ×/÷ By 10, 100, 1000, Estimation

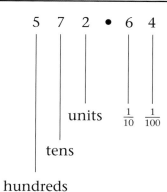

5 7 2 • 6 4

units $\frac{1}{10}$ $\frac{1}{100}$

tens

hundreds

÷ 100 digits move 2 places to the right

Examples

8400 ÷ 100 = 84   7 ÷ 100 = 0.07

Ⓜ

Give the value of the underlined figure in each of these numbers.

(1) 7.2̲   **(2)** 18̲.2   **(3)** 2̲1.6   **(4)** 4.06̲   **(5)** 5.7̲9   **(6)** 6̲.28

(7) Harry has 4 cards:

Harry may use *only 3 cards.*

   7   8   2   5

(a) What is the largest number he can make with 3 cards?

(b) What is the smallest number he can make with 3 cards?

(c) Harry has made the number ⑧②⑤. He wants to make a number ten times bigger than this. What *extra card* would he need?

(8) Tina has 4 cards:

Tina may use only 3 cards.

(a) What is the largest number she can make with 3 cards?

(b) What is the smallest number she can make with 3 cards?

Work out

(9) 36 × 100   **(11)** 27 ÷ 100   **(13)** 3.8 × 10   **(15)** 21 ÷ 100

(10) 1600 ÷ 10   **(12)** 2100 × 10   **(14)** 1.628 × 100   **(16)** 18 ÷ 10

E

Copy and complete:

1 ☐ × 10 = 6170   **4** ☐ ÷ 10 = 280   **7** 6.2 × ☐ = 620

2 ☐ × 100 = 92 000   **5** ☐ ÷ 100 = 70   **8** 19 ÷ ☐ = 0.19

3 ☐ ÷ 100 = 8   **6** ☐ × 100 = 41   **9** ☐ ÷ 100 = 1.08

Round to the nearest 10

10 136   **11** 974   **12** 587   **13** 7245

Round to the nearest 100

14 736   **15** 1147   **16** 3970   **17** 5653

Estimate Questions **18** to **21** by rounding to the nearest 10:

18 91 – 48   **19** 49 × 11   **20** 52 × 9   **21** 162 – 83

Estimate Questions **22** to **25** by rounding to the nearest whole number:

22 14.6 + 8.3   **23** 26.5 – 18.8   **24** 8.7 × 4.2   **25** 47.7 ÷ 5.9

Revision 2 – Adding, Subtracting, Multiplying, Dividing

LEARN   LEARN

```
  7 4
+ 1 8
  9 2
   1
```
Line up units with units
Line up tens with tens
Line up hundreds with hundreds

```
  ⁵ ¹
  5 6 3
  – 3 7
  5 2 6
```

183 × 32

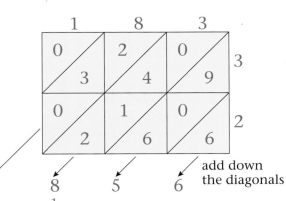

183 × 32

or

```
    1 8 3
  ×   3 2
    3 6 6  (183 × 2)
  5 4 9 0  (183 × 30)
  5 8 5 6
       1
```

add down the diagonals

so the answer is 5856

M

Work out:

(1) 538
+ 175

(2) 3269
+ 1663

(3) 648
− 475

(4) 861
− 628

(5) 9629
− 5834

(6) 8 × 3
(7) 7 × 7
(8) 9 × 6
(9) 7 × 8
(10) 8 × 6

(11) 42 ÷ 6
(12) 24 ÷ 4
(13) 28 ÷ 4
(14) 54 ÷ 6
(15) 63 ÷ 9

Copy and complete:

(16) ☐ × 6 = 54
(18) 30 ÷ ☐ = 5
(20) 21 ÷ ☐ = 7

(17) 7 × ☐ = 63
(19) 8 × ☐ = 72
(21) ☐ ÷ 4 = 6

Work out:

(22) 3)126
(23) 4)152
(24) 6)378
(25) 441 ÷ 7
(26) 297 ÷ 9

(27) Denise shares £312 equally between 4 children.
How much money does each child get?

(28) A school has 343 pupils. 228 are boys. How many girls are there?

E

Work out:

(1) 68 × 34
(3) 38 × 17
(5) 521 × 32
(7) 249 × 18

(2) 73 × 19
(4) 58 × 32
(6) 171 × 36
(8) 376 × 39

(9) A set meal in a restaurant costs £23 for each person. How much does it cost for 187 people?

(10) 18)306
(11) 24)912
(12) 928 ÷ 29
(13) 672 ÷ 32

(14) A bus can carry 52 passengers. How many buses are needed for 624 passengers?

LEARN LEARN

+	+	=	+
−	−	=	+
−	+	=	−
+	−	=	−

Remember: 'same signs: +'
'different signs: −'

(a) $-2 + (-3)$
     $= -2 - 3$
     $= -5$

(b) $4 + (-6)$
     $= 4 - 6$
     $= -2$

(c) $1 - (-3)$
     $= 1 + 3$
     $= 4$

(d) $-6 \times 4 = -24$

(e) $-6 \times -4 = 24$

(f) $-9 \times -3 = 27$

(g) $-9 \div -3 = 3$

(h) $-12 \div 3 = -4$

(i) $16 \div -4 = -4$

Division with remainders:

$$\begin{array}{r} 9\ 6 \text{ rem. } 1 \\ 4\overline{)38^25} \end{array} \quad \text{so } 385 \div 4 = 96 \text{ rem. } 1$$

M

①

London 11°C
Moscow −14°C

Athens 28°C

(a) Which temperature is the coldest?

(b) How much hotter is London than Moscow?

(c) What is the difference in temperature between Athens and Moscow?

(d) The temperature falls by 13 °C in London. What is the new temperature?

Work out:

② $-3 + 4$

④ $+2 - 8$

⑥ $-4 + 6$

⑧ $3 - 8$

⑩ $-7 + 3$

③ $+6 - 9$

⑤ $0 - 5$

⑦ $5 - 7$

⑨ $-2 - 6$

⑪ $-6 - 3$

⑫ The temperature is −14 °C. It rises by 8 °C. Find the new temperature.

Work out:

⑬ $3\overline{)278}$

⑭ $5\overline{)622}$

⑮ $8\overline{)343}$

⑯ $3\overline{)683}$

⑰ $6\overline{)454}$

E

Work out:

1 3 − (−6) **3** 8 + (−7) **5** 8 − (+5) **7** 3 + (−2) **9** −6 − (−2)

2 7 + (−4) **4** 7 − (−2) **6** 6 + (−10) **8** 6 − (−2) **10** −5 − (−4)

11 Six children can sit around a table. There are 41 children. How many tables are needed?

12 Chocolates are sold in packets of 9. How many packets can be made with 50 chocolates?

13 60 children want to play in a 7-a-side football challenge. Each team has 7 players. How many teams can be made?

Work out:

14 −8 × −3 **16** −6 × −8 **18** −5 × 6 **20** −20 ÷ 5 **22** −63 ÷ 7

15 −7 × −3 **17** 4 × −9 **19** −12 ÷ −4 **21** 426 ÷ −6 **23** −49 ÷ −7

Revision 4 – Fractions

LEARN   LEARN

More Examples

(a) $\frac{1}{5}$ of 45
  = 45 ÷ 5 = 9

(b) $\frac{3}{5}$ of 45
  = (45 ÷ 5) × 3
  = 9 × 3 = 27

(c) $\frac{2}{5} + \frac{1}{5} = \frac{3}{5}$

(d) $\frac{8}{9} - \frac{4}{9} = \frac{4}{9}$

M

Copy and complete:

1 $\frac{2}{3} = \frac{\square}{9}$

3 $\frac{7}{10} = \frac{28}{\square}$

5 $\frac{\square}{9} = \frac{15}{27}$

7 $\frac{6}{7} = \frac{30}{\square}$

9 $\frac{\square}{10} = \frac{24}{80}$

2 $\frac{1}{4} = \frac{\square}{20}$

4 $\frac{\square}{4} = \frac{6}{8}$

6 $\frac{5}{8} = \frac{\square}{24}$

8 $\frac{4}{9} = \frac{24}{\square}$

10 $\frac{1}{3} = \frac{\square}{18}$

162

(11) Which fraction is the larger? $\frac{3}{4}$ or $\frac{2}{3}$

(12) Which fraction is the larger? $\frac{7}{10}$ or $\frac{4}{5}$

(13)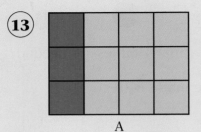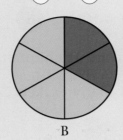

A   B

What fraction is shaded in each of the diagrams A and B?

Which fraction is the larger?

Cancel the fractions below:

(14) $\frac{8}{16}$ **(15)** $\frac{9}{15}$ **(16)** $\frac{10}{30}$ **(17)** $\frac{15}{40}$ **(18)** $\frac{3}{12}$ **(19)** $\frac{12}{20}$ **(20)** $\frac{20}{25}$

E

Work out:

(1) $\frac{1}{8}$ of 24 **(3)** $\frac{1}{4}$ of 20 **(5)** $\frac{1}{8}$ of 32 **(7)** $\frac{3}{7}$ of 42 **(9)** $\frac{7}{10}$ of 90

(2) $\frac{3}{8}$ of 24 **(4)** $\frac{3}{4}$ of 20 **(6)** $\frac{5}{8}$ of 32 **(8)** $\frac{5}{9}$ of 54 **(10)** $\frac{4}{5}$ of 30

(11) Calli has 48 old CDs. She gives away $\frac{3}{8}$ of these CDs. How many CDs does she give away?

(12) A petrol tank in a car holds 63 litres when full. How much petrol is in the tank when it is $\frac{4}{9}$ full?

Work out:

(13) $\frac{1}{7} + \frac{2}{7}$ **(14)** $\frac{3}{11} + \frac{4}{11}$ **(15)** $\frac{7}{9} - \frac{2}{9}$ **(16)** $\frac{9}{20} - \frac{8}{20}$ **(17)** $\frac{3}{10} + \frac{6}{10}$

LEARN

$$3.6 + 9$$

$$3.6$$
$$+ 9.0$$
$$\overline{12.6}$$
$$_1$$

For adding and subtracting, line up the decimal point.

$$8.6 - 2.17$$

$$8.\overset{5\;1}{\cancel{6}0}$$
$$-2.17$$
$$\overline{6.43}$$

LEARN

£2.2**1** × 4 = £8.8**4**

$$221$$
$$\times\ \ 4$$
$$\overline{884}$$

£6.42 ÷ 3 = £2.14

$$2.14$$
$$3\overline{)6.4^12}$$

M

Write these decimals as fractions:

1 0.7   **2** 0.03   **3** 0.9   **4** 0.21   **5** 0.73

Write these fractions as decimals:

6 $\frac{8}{100}$ **7** $\frac{6}{10}$ **8** $\frac{4}{10}$ **9** $\frac{13}{100}$ **10** $\frac{31}{100}$

Arrange the decimals below in order. Start with the smallest:

11 0.06   0.062   0.602   0.6   0.006

12 0.17   0.107   0.007   0.1   0.07

13 7.73   8.7   7.83   8.37   8.73

14 Which decimal is the larger? 0.9 or 0.09

15 Which decimal is the larger? 0.4 or 0.043

E

1 6.81 + 3.18   **5** 8.1 – 2.63   **9** £3.64 × 4   **13** £3.87 × 6   **17** £9.48 ÷ 6

2 4.7 + 9   **6** 3.4 – 0.27   **10** £2.86 × 3   **14** £6.30 ÷ 5   **18** £9.73 ÷ 7

3 5.6 + 6 + 2.1   **7** 81 – 7.6   **11** £4.11 × 5   **15** £8.96 ÷ 4

4 6.28 – 3.43   **8** 32 – 12.7   **12** £5.62 × 7   **16** £9.90 ÷ 10

LEARN   LEARN

1% means '÷ 100'   1% of 300 = 300 ÷ 100 = 3

10% means '÷ 10'   10% of 300 = 300 ÷ 10 = 30

(Note. 50% = $\frac{1}{2}$ 25% = $\frac{1}{4}$ 75% = $\frac{3}{4}$)

Use 1% and 10% to find the other percentages

Examples

(a)   Find 3% of 400

     1% of 400 = 400 ÷ 100 = 4

     3% of 400 = 4 × 3 = 12

            ↑
            1%

(b)   Find 20% of 70

     10% of 70 = 70 ÷ 10 = 7

     20% of 70 = 7 × 2 = 14

            ↑
            10%

(c)   4% of 28

     1% of 28 = 28 ÷ 100 = 0.28

     4% of 28 = 0.28 × 4 = 1.12

            ↑
            1%

Ⓜ
Work out:

(1)   10% of 700

(2)   30% of 80

(3)   20% of 90

(4)   10% of 35

(5)   20% of 35

(6)   25% of 48

(7)   1% of 400

(8)   7% of 400

(9)   1% of 730

(10)   3% of 730

(11)   1% of 68

(12)   4% of 68

(13)
SHIRTS
£20
30% OFF
Find the sale price.

(14)
TV
£320
5% OFF
Find the sale price.

(15)
TROUSERS
£40
15% OFF
Find the sale price.

(16)   Increase £64 by 1%.

(17)   Decrease £36 by 4%.

(18)   Reduce £64 by 3%.

Change the following ratios to their simplest form:

1 6 : 3   **2** 10 : 25   **3** 9 : 15   **4** 21 : 35   **5** 8 : 24

Divide each amount of money below in the ratio given:

6 £35, 2 : 3   **8** £80, 5 : 3   **10** £60, 5 : 3 : 4

7 £50, 9 : 1   **9** £100, 3 : 17   **11** £200, 31 : 4 : 15

12 If seven pencils cost 77p, how much will nine pencils cost?

13 If five chews cost 60p, how much will six chews cost?

14 If four bars of chocolate cost £1.80, how much will nine bars of chocolate cost?

15 If ten calculators cost £50, how much will thirteen calculators cost?

16 £2000 is to be shared out between Carl and Simone in the ratio 9 : 11. How much money does each person get?

Revision 7 – Sequences, Factors, Multiples, Primes, Square Numbers

A *prime* number can only be divided exactly by two different numbers (these are the number 1 and itself).

A *factor* is a number which divides exactly into another number (there is no remainder).

A *multiple* of 5 is any number in the 5 times table.

Examples

(a) 7, 14, 21 and 28 are all multiples of 7.

(b) 7 is a prime number (ony 1 and 7 can divide exactly into 7).

(c) All the factors of 6 are 1, 2, 3 and 6.

16 is a square number because 4 × 4 = 16.

We say $4^2 = 4 \times 4 = 16$.

The square root of 9 is 3 because 3 × itself = 9.

We say $\sqrt{9} = 3$.

M

Copy and complete:

(1) 11, 15, ☐, 23, ☐

(2) 22, 17, ☐, 7, ☐

(3) 1, 4, 9, 16, ☐, ☐

(4) 80, 40, 20, ☐, ☐

(5) –16, ☐, –10, –7, ☐

(6) 2, 3, 5, 7, ☐, ☐

Write down *all* the factors of:

(7) 10 (4 factors)

(8) 24 (8 factors)

(9) 14

(10) 36

(11) Write down four multiples of 6.

(12) Write down four multiples of 8.

(13) Write down six multiples of 10.

(14) Which of these numbers are prime?

(15) Is 63 a multiple of 7?

(16) Is 160 a multiple of 20?

(17) Is 74 a multiple of 4?

11   22
14
8   13   19
5   20

E

Work out:

(1) 7^2

(2) 8^2

(3) 10^2

(4) $\sqrt{81}$

(5) $\sqrt{4}$

(6) $\sqrt{36}$

(7) $\sqrt{100} - \sqrt{1}$

(8) $\sqrt{64} - \sqrt{25}$

(9) $\sqrt{(40 - 24)}$

(10) $3^2 + 7^2$

(11) $9^2 - 2^2$

(12) $\sqrt{(3^2 + 4^2)}$

What number belongs in the empty box below:

(13) 1, 2, 4 and 8 are all the factors of ☐

(14) 1, 5 and 25 are all the factors of ☐

(15) 6, 12, 24 and 42 are all multiples of ☐

(16) 16, 24, 32 and 40 are all multiples of ☐

(17) Is 18 a prime number?

(18) Copy and complete:

1, 3, 6, 10, ☐, ☐, ☐

M

Draw a 12 × 12 grid as shown.

Plot each set of points to make letters.

(4, 8) (2, 8) (2, 11)

(8, 8) (8, 6) (7, 8) (7, 6)

(7, 1) (7, 5) (9, 5)
(9, 1) (9, 3) (7, 3)

(6, 4) (5, 3) (4, 4)
(5, 5) (4, 4) (3, 5) (4, 6)

(6, 9) (8, 11) (6, 11)
(10, 11) (10, 9) (8, 9) (8, 11)

Arrange the letters to make a very important word!

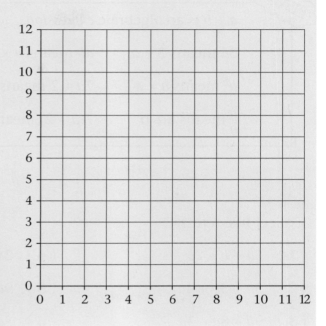

E

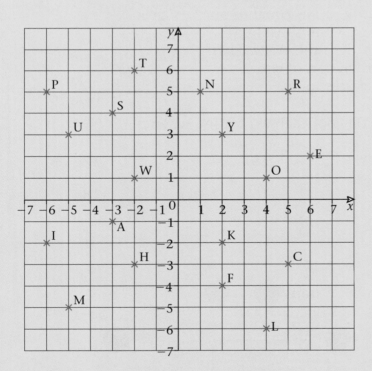

Use the grid to spell out this important message. Read across.

(2, 3) (4, 1) (−5, 3)   (2, −2) (1, 5) (4, 1) (−2, 1)   (−6, −2) (−2, 6)
(−5, −5) (−3, −1) (2, −2) (6, 2) (−3, 4)   (−3, 4) (6, 2) (1, 5) (−3, 4) (6, 2)   (−2, 6) (4, 1)
(4, −6) (6, 2) (−3, −1) (5, 5) (1, 5)!

LEARN

a + b is an algebraic *expression*.

3*a* means 3 × *a*   *ab* means *a* × *b*

a² means *a* × *a*   7*a* + 2 means '7 × *a* then add 2'

$\frac{a}{b}$ means a ÷ b   7(*a* + 2) means '*a* + 2 then multiply by 7'

LEARN

Ⓜ

Collect like terms:

① 6*a* + *b* + 2*b*

② 5*a* + 3*b* + 4*a*

③ 9*a* + 8*a* – 3*a*

④ 2*b* + 7*c* – 3*c*

⑤ 9*a* + 3*a* + 2

⑥ 5*x* + 9 – 2*x*

⑦ 6*c* + 4*d* + 7

⑧ 3*c* + 6*c* + 2

⑨ 8 + 3*a* – 2

⑩

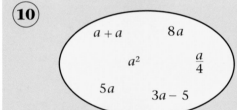

Each expression inside one ring is equal to one expression inside the other ring. Write down each pair of equal expressions.

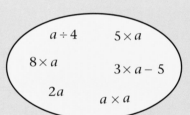

In Questions ⑪ to ⑱, find the value of each expression when *a* = 5, *b* = 3 and *c* = 2.

⑪ 5*a*

⑫ 4*c*

⑬ 5*a* + 4*c*

⑭ *b²*

⑮ $\frac{10b}{a}$

⑯ 4(*b* + *c*)

⑰ *bc*

⑱ *c*(3*b* + *a*)

Ⓔ

Find the perimeter of the shapes in Questions ① to ③ :

①

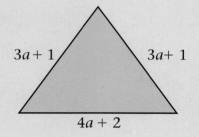

②

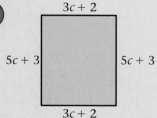

③

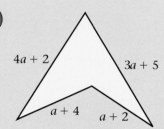

In Questions ④ to ⑫ you are given a formula. Find the value of the letter required in each Question.

④ $a = 5b + 2$ Find a when $b = 3$.

⑤ $m = 6n + 7$ Find m when $n = 2$.

⑥ $p = 2s + 1$ Find p when $s = 8$.

⑦ $x = y^2$ Find x when $y = 7$.

⑧ $a = b^2 + c$ Find a when $b = 6$ and $c = 8$.

⑨ $c = 2(5d - 1)$ Find c when $d = 2$.

⑩ $x = yz$ Find x when $y = 7$ and $z = 16$.

⑪ $a = \dfrac{b + c}{10}$ Find a when $b = 16$ and $c = 34$.

⑫ $y = \dfrac{x^2 + x}{5}$ Find y when $x = 4$.

Revision 10 – Equations and Brackets

'Solve' $x + 3 = 8$ means 'find the value of x'.
The answer is $x = 5$.

Examples

(a) Solve $n - 6 = 8$

$n = 14$

because $\boxed{14} - 6 = 8$

(b) Solve $3x + 5 = 17$

$3x = 12$

$x = 4$

because $3 \times \boxed{4} + 5 = 17$

(c) Solve $4k - 3 = 17$

$4k = 20$

$k = 5$

because $4 \times \boxed{5} - 3 = 17$

(d) Solve $5n + 3 = 2n + 21$

(Subtract $2n$ from both sides)

$3n + 3 = 21$

(Subtract 3 from both sides)

$3n = 18$

$n = 6$

because $3 \times \boxed{6} = 18$

A number in front of brackets, multiplies each of the numbers or symbols inside the brackets.

Examples

(a) $7(a + 3)$

$= 7 \times a + 7 \times 3$

$= 7a + 21$

(b) $3(x - 4)$

$= 3x - 12$

(c) $5(2a + 3)$

$= 10a + 15$

M

Solve the equations below:

(1) $n + 2 = 7$

(2) $n + 21 = 34$

(3) $n - 7 = 10$

(4) $17 = x + 5$

(5) $x - 12 = 15$

(6) $5n = 10$

(7) $7n = 42$

(8) $2n + 1 = 13$

(9) $5x + 6 = 41$

(10) $2x - 1 = 13$

(11) $3x - 6 = 18$

(12) $6x + 11 = 47$

(13) $4k + 7 = 35$

(14) $7k - 9 = 54$

(15) $6k - 16 = 44$

E

In Questions (1) to (9), multiply out the brackets:

(1) $6(x + 2)$

(2) $5(x + 4)$

(3) $7(x - 3)$

(4) $3(n - 3)$

(5) $6(3n + 2)$

(6) $2(4n - 1)$

(7) $2(3x + 2)$

(8) $7(2x - 3)$

(9) $8(5x - 6)$

Solve the equations below:

(10) $5n + 2 = 2n + 8$

(11) $4n + 7 = 2n + 19$

(12) $6x + 4 = 3x + 25$

(13) $8x + 11 = 2x + 35$

(14) $7n + 4 = 3n + 32$

(15) $9n + 20 = 5n + 32$

(16) Joe thinks of a number, doubles it and adds 7. The answer is 25. What was Joe's number?

(17) Hannah thinks of a number, trebles it and adds 11. The answer is 35. What was Hannah's number?

LEARN   LEARN

length	mass	capacity
10 mm = 1 cm	1000 g = 1 kg	1000 ml = 1 litre
100 cm = 1 m	1000 kg = 1 tonne (1 t)	

Metric/imperial units.

1 inch is about 2.5 cm   1 kg is about 2.2 pounds
1 foot is about 30 cm   1 litre is about 1.8 pints
1 mile is about 1.6 km   1 gallon is about 4.5 litres

M

Copy and complete:

(1) 5 km = ☐ m   (5) 70 mm = ☐ cm   (9) 8.5 l = ☐ ml

(2) 3.7 km = ☐ m   (6) 7.5 kg = ☐ g   (10) 7.15 l = ☐ ml

(3) 2900 m = ☐ km   (7) 8.23 kg = ☐ g   (11) 4600 ml = ☐ l

(4) 3.5 m = ☐ cm   (8) 300 g = ☐ kg   (12) 260 ml = ☐ l

(13) A ribbon is 1.8 m long. 62 cm are cut off. How long is the ribbon which is left?

(14) There is 48 cm between the top of a wardrobe and the ceiling. The room has a height of 2.2 metres. How tall is the wardrobe?

(15) One tin of peas weighs 300 g. What do 15 tins weigh in *kilograms*?

(16) A bottle contains 2 litres of cola. Six 200 ml cups are filled from the bottle. How much cola is left?

E   *You may use a calculator.* Use the numbers in the box above. Copy and complete:

(1) 3 inches are about ☐ cm.   (6) 8 kg are about ☐ pounds.

(2) 7 feet are about ☐ cm.   (7) 135 litres are about ☐ gallons.

(3) 8 litres are about ☐ pints.   (8) 70 cm are about ☐ inches.

(4) 3 gallons are about ☐ litres.   (9) 33 pounds are about ☐ kg.

(5) 100 miles are about ☐ km.   (10) 56 km are about ☐ miles.

(11) The distance from Bath to Wells is about 20 miles. How many km is this?

In Questions (12) to (14), which amount is larger?

(12) 20 inches or 48 cm?   (13) 5 gallons or 25 litres?   (14) 50 km or 35 miles?

24-hour clocks always have four digits on display.
A 24-hour clock displays midnight as 00:00.

Example

(a)   7:28 a.m. = 07:28   (b)   5:16 p.m. = 17:16

⇑   24-hour   ⇑

before noon   clock time.   after noon

Ⓜ

①   Copy and complete the table showing
12-hour and 24-hour clock times.

12-hour clock	24-hour clock
4:25 p.m	
10:30 a.m	
7:15 p.m	
	08:42
	21:06
2:55 a.m	
	11:37
	17:21
7:49 a.m	
	23:11

②   Sam travels to London on the train. The train leaves at 09:45 and arrives in London at
11:20. How long was the train journey?

③   A steamroller takes $2\frac{1}{2}$ minutes to go along a road.
How long is that in seconds?

④   A television program is 45 minutes long. It starts at 17:50. When does the program end?

⑤   If July 1st falls on a Friday, on what day will these dates fall:

(a)   July 12th   (b)   July 23rd   (c)   August 7th   (d)   June 16th

E

1 Write the following as 24-hour clock times:

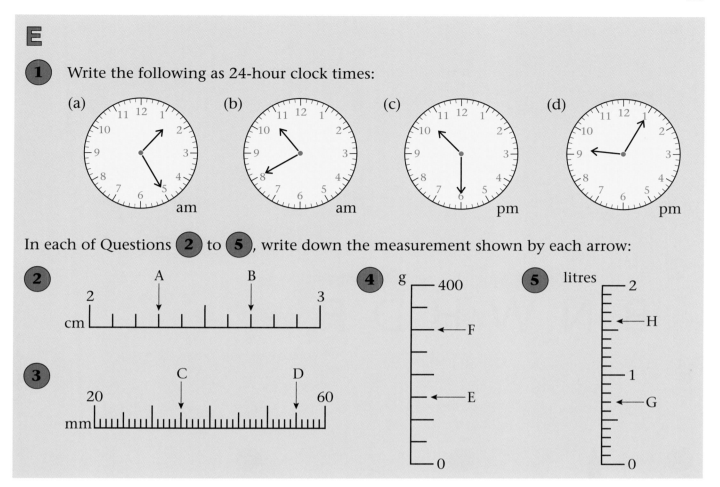

(a) ... am   (b) ... am   (c) ... pm   (d) ... pm

In each of Questions **2** to **5**, write down the measurement shown by each arrow:

2   A   B
2 |_|_|_|_|_|_|_|_| 3
cm

4 g
400
F
E
0

5 litres
2
H
1
G
0

3   C   D
20 |‖‖‖‖‖‖‖‖‖‖‖‖| 60
mm

Revision 13 – Shapes and Symmetry

A shape has line symmetry if half of its shape matches the other half exactly.

A shape has *rotational symmetry* if it fits onto itself when rotated (turned) before it gets back to its starting position.

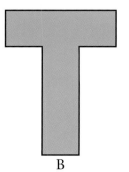

one line of symmetry

Shape A fits onto itself three times when rotated through a complete turn. We say it has rotational symmetry of *order 3*.

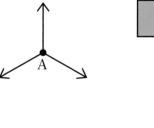

Shape B can only fit onto itself in its starting position. We say it has rotational symmetry of *order 1*.

M

For each solid below, write down the number of (a) vertices (b) faces (c) edges:

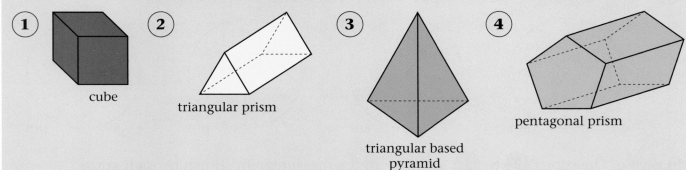

① cube

② triangular prism

③ triangular based pyramid

④ pentagonal prism

⑤ How many lines of symmetry does each letter below have?

B N W H D F

E

For each shape below write down the order of rotational symmetry (use tracing paper to help):

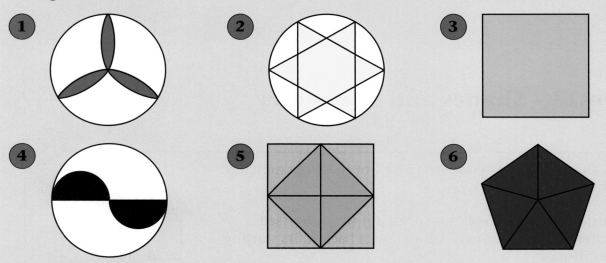

① ② ③

④ ⑤ ⑥

Copy the patterns below on squared paper. Shade in as many squares as necessary to complete the symmetrical patterns. The dotted lines are lines of symmetry.

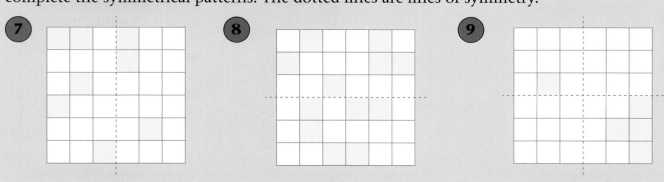

⑦ ⑧ ⑨

'Translating' a shape means moving it in a straight line.

Example

Translate the blue shape left 5 squares, up 2 squares.

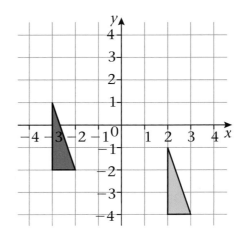

'Rotating' a shape means turning a shape around a point.

Use tracing paper

Rotate the red shape 90° clockwise about the point A.

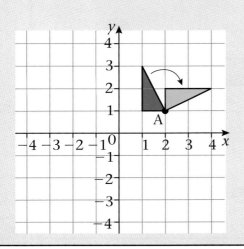

M

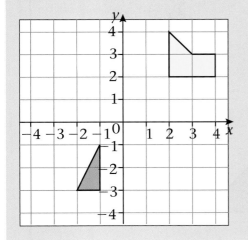

(1) Copy the grid and the pentagon.

Translate the shape 3 different times.

(a) left 4, down 1   (b) left 1, down 4

(c) left 3, down 3.

(2) Copy the grid and the triangle.

Translate the shape 3 different times.

(a) left 1, up 1   (b) right 3, down 1

(c) right 4, up 4.

Copy each shape in Questions ③ to ⑤ and the mirror line.

Draw the *reflection* of each shape in the mirror line.

③ 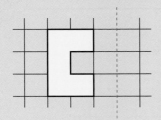 ④ 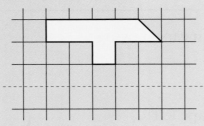 ⑤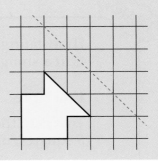

E

Copy each shape in Questions ① to ④ . You can use tracing paper. For each shape:

(a) *rotate* the shape 90° about point A in a clockwise direction.

(b) *rotate* the shape 180° about point A.

① 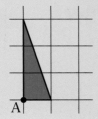 ② 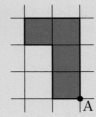 ③ 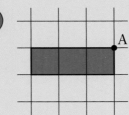 ④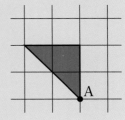

Revision 15 – Perimeter, Area, Volume

The *perimeter* of a shape is the distance around its edges.

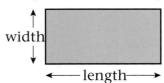

area of rectangle = length × width

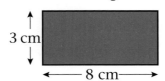

area = 3 × 8 = 24 cm²
perimeter = 3 + 8 + 3 + 8 = 22 cm

area of triangle = $\frac{1}{2}$ (base × height)

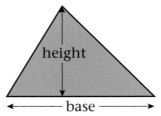

volume of a cuboid = length × width × height

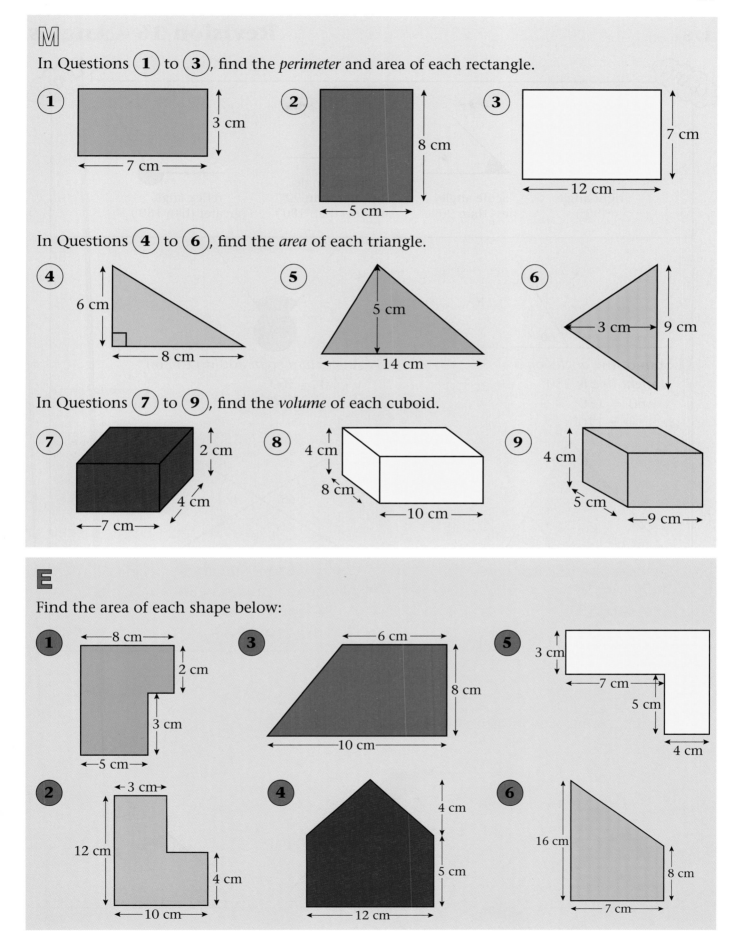

M

In Questions **1** to **3**, find the *perimeter* and area of each rectangle.

1 3 cm, 7 cm

2 8 cm, 5 cm

3 7 cm, 12 cm

In Questions **4** to **6**, find the *area* of each triangle.

4 6 cm, 8 cm

5 5 cm, 14 cm

6 3 cm, 9 cm

In Questions **7** to **9**, find the *volume* of each cuboid.

7 2 cm, 4 cm, 7 cm

8 4 cm, 8 cm, 10 cm

9 4 cm, 5 cm, 9 cm

E

Find the area of each shape below:

1 8 cm, 2 cm, 3 cm, 5 cm

2 3 cm, 12 cm, 4 cm, 10 cm

3 6 cm, 8 cm, 10 cm

4 4 cm, 5 cm, 12 cm

5 3 cm, 7 cm, 5 cm, 4 cm

6 16 cm, 8 cm, 7 cm

LEARN   LEARN

  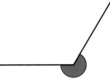

right angle   acute angle   obtuse angle   reflex angle
(90°)   (less than 90°)   (greater than 90°   (greater than 180°)
                                        and less than 180°)

Sum of the *angles on a*
straight line is 180°
$x + 60° = 180°$
$x = 120°$

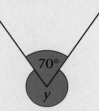

Angles at a point add up to 360°
$y + 70° = 360°$
$y = 290°$

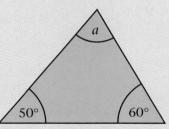

Sum of the *angles in a*
triangle is 180°
$a + 110° = 180°$
$a = 70°$

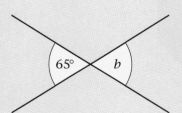

When two lines intersect,
the opposite angles are equal
$b = 65°$
The angles 65° and *b* are *vertically opposite*.

M

(1) Using a protractor, measure the angles a, b, c, d and e.

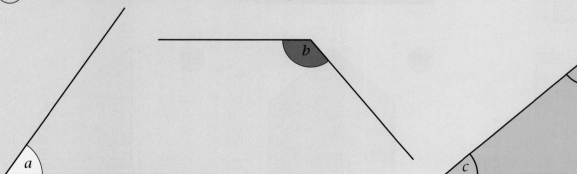

Draw the following angles. Label each angle acute, obtuse or reflex.

(2) 75°   (4) 130°   (6) 240°   (8) 160°

(3) 80°   (5) 25°   (7) 42°

E

Find the angles marked with the letters.

1

4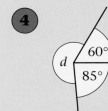

7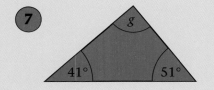

10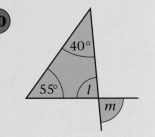

2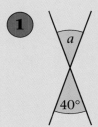

5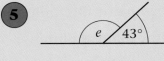

8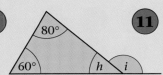

11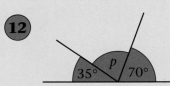

3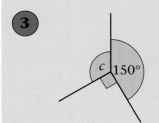

6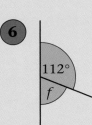

9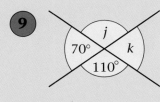

12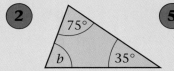

Revision 17 – Pictograms and Grouping Data

The ages of 20 people are shown below:

28	7	21	32	11
23	14	38	9	16
32	27	16	18	21
19	34	23	27	2

We can group this data using a tally chart.

Age	Tally	Frequency
0 – 9	|||	3
10 – 19	卌		6
20 – 29	卌 ||	7
30 – 39	||||	4

M

1 Here are the ages of 25 people at a party:

17	16	28	22	31
52	29	31	27	40
38	53	18	21	18
29	17	22	19	17
41	37	33	28	22

(a) Copy and complete the chart below:

Age	Tally	Frequency
10 – 19		
20 – 29		
30 – 39		
40 – 49		
50 – 59		

(b) Draw a frequency diagram to show the data.

2 This pictogram show the number of children absent from school on each day of one week.

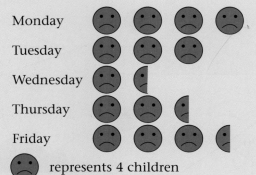

Monday
Tuesday
Wednesday
Thursday
Friday

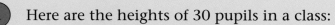 represents 4 children

(a) How many children were absent on Tuesday?

(b) How many children were absent on Wednesday?

(c) How many *more* children were absent on Friday than Thursday?

E

1 Here are the heights of 30 pupils in a class:

147	155	145	152	149	146
152	147	143	147	148	148
151	151	144	157	141	158
145	147	151	144	146	146
147	148	143	150	154	149

(a) Copy and complete the chart below:

Height	Tally	Frequency
140 – 144		
145 – 149		
150 – 154		
155 – 159		

(b) Draw a frequency diagram to show this data.

6 children get the following pocket money:

$$3, \quad 10, \quad 6, \quad 9, \quad 6, \quad 8$$

(a) *Mode* = 6 because there are more 6's than any other number.

(b) *Median*: Arrange the numbers in order: 3 6 6 8 9 10

The median is the $\frac{1}{2}$-way number

$$\text{Median} = \frac{6+8}{2} = 7$$

(c) *Mean* = $\dfrac{3 + 10 + 6 + 9 + 6 + 8}{6} = \dfrac{42}{6} = 7$

6 numbers on the list

(d) *Range* = highest number – lowest number = 10 – 3 = 7

To compare 2 sets of data, always write at *least 2 things*:

1) Compare an *average* (i.e. mean, median or mode)

2) Compare the *range* of each set of data (this shows how spread out the data is).

Ⓜ

For each list of numbers below, find the   (a) mode   (b) median   (c) mean   (d) range.

① 1, 5, 6, 11, 3, 4, 5

② 2, 4, 2, 8, 4, 2, 7, 4, 5, 2

③ 8, 6, 8, 6, 8, 6

④ 5, 3, 7, 2, 5, 7, 8, 10, 7

⑤ Write down 3 members with a mean of 4.

⑥ Write down 6 numbers with a range of 10.

E

1 Children in class 9C and 9D have a maths test. The marks for 10 children from each class are shown below:

Class 9C: 8 7 6 6 9 6 4 7 2 5   Class 9D: 4 7 3 9 9 8 6 9 8 7

Copy and complete the statements below to compare the test marks in class 9C and class 9D.

Class 9C: mean = _____ range = _____   Class 9D: mean = _____ range = _____

'The mean test mark for class 9C is (*greater/smaller*) than the mean test mark for class 9D. The range of the test marks for class 9C is (*greater/smaller*) than the range for class 9D (i.e. test marks in class 9C are (*more/less*) spread out).

2 Data A: 8 7 5 1 9   Data B: 6 8 2 1 3

Find the median and range for each of Data A and Data B. Write two sentences to compare Data A and Data B (one sentence using the medians and one sentence using the ranges).

Revision 19 – Pie Charts and Stem/Leaf Diagrams

LEARN   LEARN

A survey about favourite colours was done.
The results are below:

Colour	Frequency (number of people)
red	15
yellow	19
blue	7
green	4

Draw a pie chart to show this information.

Method

(a)   Add all the numbers:
15 +19 + 7 + 4 = 45 people.

(b)   Whole angle 360° must be split between 45 people.
Angle for each person = 360° ÷ 45 = 8°

(c)   Angle for 'red' = 15 × 8° = 120°
Angle for 'yellow' = 19 × 8° = 152°
Angle for 'blue' = 7 × 8° = 56°
Angle for 'green' = 4 × 8° = 32°.

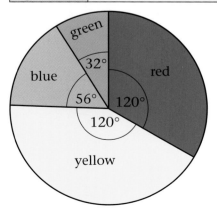

Ⓜ

① The pie chart shows the favourite food of 24 people. Write down each type of food and how many people chose each food.

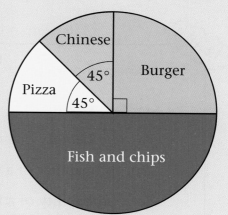

In Questions ② to ③ work out the angle for each item and draw a pie chart.

② Most popular school subject.

Subject	Frequency
art	16
history	7
science	12
maths	15
P.E.	10

③ Most popular pastime.

Pastime	Frequency
watching TV	21
sport	16
skateboarding	11
computer games	23
others	19

Ⓔ

① Draw a stem and leaf diagram for each set of data below:

(a)
30	47	35	54	52	22	53	41
44	28	47	29	59	38	46	57

(b)
45	25	61	58	37	40	55	31
39	67	59	22	38	63	25	68
52	67	24	44	33	51	46	45

② Here is a stem and leaf diagram showing the test marks of some pupils.

(a) Write down the range of the test marks.

(b) How many pupils did the test?

(c) What is the median test mark?

Stem	Leaf
3	4 9
4	1 2 2 6 8
5	1 5 6 6 9
6	0 3 8 9
7	3 7
8	4

Key 6|3 = 63

LEARN   LEARN

Expected probability = $\dfrac{\text{the number of ways the event can happen}}{\text{the number of possible outcomes}}$

Examples

(a)   probability of a coin landing on heads is $\frac{1}{2}$.

(b)   probability of a fair dice landing on a '2' is $\frac{1}{6}$.

(c)   probability of a fair dice landing on an 'even' number is $\frac{3}{6}$

($\frac{3}{6}$ is cancelled to $\frac{1}{2}$).

M

(1)   Amy has some bags with some black beads and some white beads. She is going to take a bead from each bag without looking.

A   B   C   D   E

Copy and complete each statement below:

(a)   It is *impossible* that Amy will take a black bead from bag . . . .

(b)   It is *equally likely* that Amy will take a black bead or a white bead from bag
. . . .

(c)   It is *likely* that Amy will take a black bead from bag . . . .

(d)   It is *certain* that Amy will take a black bead from bag . . . .

(e)   It is *unlikely* that Amy will take a black bead from bag . . . .

(2)   (a)

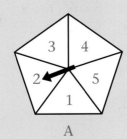 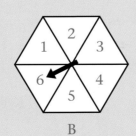

A   B

Which spinner gives you the best chance to get 1?

Explain *why* you chose that answer.

(b)

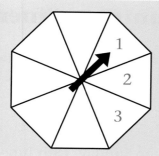

Each section of this spinner is the same size.

Write down which numbers are missing so that both of these statements are true:

'It is *equally likely* that you will spin 2 or 3' and 'It is *more likely* that you will spin 4 than 3'.

There are two possible answers.

E

1 A pencil case contains pencils of the following colours: 4 blue, 3 red, 2 green and 2 yellow. One pencil is selected without looking. Find the probability that the pencil is

(a) blue

(b) yellow

(c) red or blue.

2 One card is selected at random from the nine cards shown.

Find the probability of selecting

(a) the ace of diamonds

(b) a king

(c) an ace

3 A hat contains 6 balls. One ball is white, the rest are red. One ball is chosen at random. Find the probability that the ball is   (a)   white   (b)   red.

4 Write down the probability of rolling a fair dice and getting a '4'.

5 Write down the probability of rolling a fair dice and getting a '7'.

6 A bag contains the balls shown. One ball is taken out at random. Find the probability that it is

(a) blue

(b) red

(c) yellow

(d) pink

B = blue
R = red
Y = yellow

The charts below show how many adults and children went to Halchester cinema during two separate weeks.

Key: adults   children

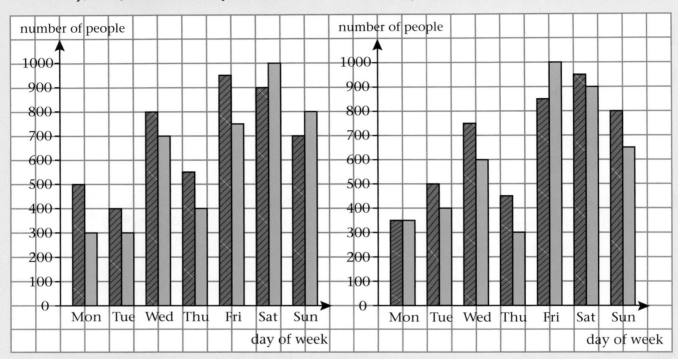

Monday, 5th June to Sunday, 11th June   Monday, 12th June to Sunday, 18th June

Cost of a ticket

	adult	child
Mon to Thu	£7.75	£6.25
Fri to Sun	£8.75	£6.75

Cinema Profit

20% of the total ticket sales

Part A

1. How many adults went to the cinema on 7th June?

2. How many children went to the cinema on 16th June?

3. How many adults in total went to the cinema from Monday, 5th June to the following Thursday?

4. How many children in total went to the cinema from Friday, 9th June to Sunday, 11th June?

Part B

1. What was the total ticket money paid by the adults from Monday, 5th June to the following Thursday?

2. What was the total ticket money paid by the adults from Friday, 9th June to the following Sunday?

3. What was the total ticket money paid by the children from Monday, 5th June to the following Thursday?

4. What was the total ticket money paid by the children from Friday, 9th June to the following Sunday?

5. What was the total ticket money taken by the cinema from Monday, 5th June to Sunday, 11th June?

Part C

What was the total ticket money taken by the cinema from Monday, 12th June to Sunday, 18th June?

Part D

How much profit did the cinema make from Monday, 5th June to Sunday, 18th June?

You must not use a calculator.

1 Copy and write in the boxes what the missing numbers could be.

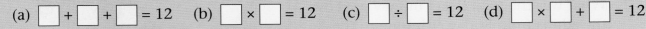

(a) ☐ + ☐ + ☐ = 12 (b) ☐ × ☐ = 12 (c) ☐ ÷ ☐ = 12 (d) ☐ × ☐ + ☐ = 12

2 (a) Tom asked 35 pupils if they travel to school by bus. 25 pupils said *yes*. 10 pupils said *no*.

He started to draw a pictogram using the key ⊠ represents 5 pupils.

Copy and complete the pictogram to show Tom's results.

(b) Sarah asked 24 pupils which subject they like best. She drew this pictogram but forgot to write the key.

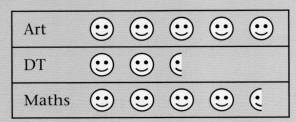

How many pupils does 🙂 represent?

3 (a) Look at this scale.

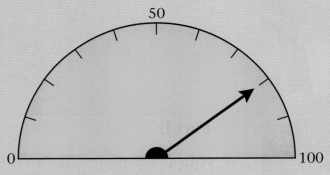

What value is the arrow pointing to on the scale?

(b) Here is a different scale.

Copy and draw an arrow (↓) so that it shows the same value as the arrow in part a).

4 (a) What number should you *add to 38* to make *100*?

(b) What number should you *subtract from* 100 to *make 68*?

(c) Work out 36 + 37.

(d) Work out 72 ÷ 3.

(e) Work out 1036 + 309.

(f) Work out 3736 – 570.

5 Look at these prices.

Pencil	25p
Blue pen	45p
Green pen	50p
Ruler	20p
Eraser	30p

(a) Find the total cost of two rulers and one pencil.

(b) Find the total cost of three blue pens.

(c) The total cost of one blue pen and ☐ is 75p.
Which item belongs in the box?

(d) There are many *different ways* to make the total cost *70p*.
Use the prices above.
Copy and complete the boxes below. One way is done for you.

70p
→ The total cost of | two pencils and a ruler |
→ The total cost of | |
→ The total cost of | |
→ The total cost of | |

6 (a) The number chain below is part of a *doubling* number chain. Write down the two missing numbers.

☐ → 30 → 60 → 120 → ☐

(b) The number chain below is part of a halving number chain. Write down the two missing numbers.

24 → 12 → 6 → ☐ → ☐

7 (a) My wall clock shows this time:
Which *two* of the digital clocks below could be showing the *same time* as my wall clock?

| 04:00 | 13:00 | 14:00 | 15:00 | 16:00 |
| A | B | C | D | E |

(b) Early in the *morning* my
wall clock shows this time:

morning

Write what time my digital clock is showing.

┌─────────┐
│   :   │
└─────────┘

(c) In the *afternoon* my
wall clock shows this time:

afternoon

Write down what time my digital clock is now showing.

┌─────────┐
│   :   │
└─────────┘

8 A teacher has six number cards. He says:
'I am going to take a card at random.
Each card shows a *different* positive whole number.
It is *certain* that the card will show a number less than 12.
It is *impossible* that the card will show an even number.'
What numbers are on the cards?

┌───┐ ┌───┐ ┌───┐ ┌───┐ ┌───┐ ┌───┐
│   │ │   │ │   │ │   │ │   │ │   │
└───┘ └───┘ └───┘ └───┘ └───┘ └───┘

9 When the wind blows it feels colder.
The stronger the wind, the colder it feels.
Write down the three missing numbers in the table below.

Wind strength	Temperature out of the wind (°C)	How much colder it feels in the wind (°C)	Temperature it feels in the wind (°C)
Moderate breeze	6	8 degrees colder	–2
Fresh breeze	–6	12 degrees colder	☐
Strong breeze	–7	☐ degrees colder	–20
Gale	☐	24 degrees colder	–47

10 Look at the hexagon and the triangle.

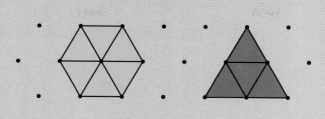

(a) Do the hexagon and triangle have the *same area*?
   Explain your answer.
(b) Do the hexagon and triangle have the *same perimeter*?
   Explain your answer.

11 There are two small tins and one big tin on these scales.

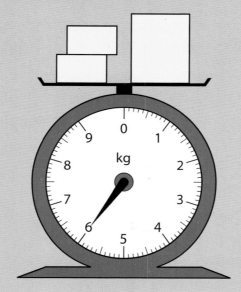

The two small tins each have the same mass.
The mass of the big tin is *3.2 kg*.
What is the mass of *one small tin*?

12 Some pupils throw two fair six-sided dice.
Each dice is numbered 1 to 6. One dice is blue.
The other dice is red.
Sonia's dice show *blue 4, red 3*.
Her *total score* is 7.
The cross on the grid shows her throw.

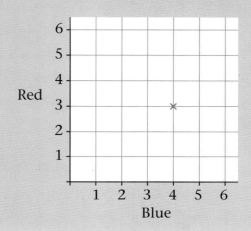

(a) Copy the grid below:

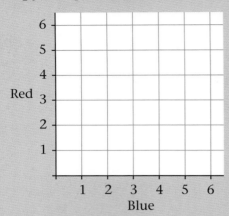

Jake's *total score* is 5.

What numbers could Jake's dice show?

Put crosses on the grid to show *all* the different pairs of numbers Jake's dice could show.

(b) The pupils play a game.

| Winning rule: | Win a point if the number on the *blue* dice is the *same as* the number on the *red* dice. |

Copy this grid and put crosses on the grid to show *all* the different winning throws.

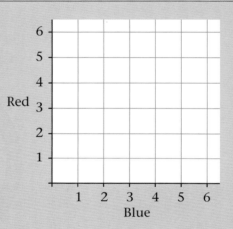

(c) The pupils play a different game.

The grid shows all the different winning throws.

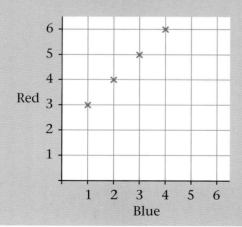

Copy and complete the sentence below to show the winning rule.

| Winning rule: | Win a point if the number on the blue dice is _ |

13 Simplify these expressions:

$$4k + 5 + 3k =$$
$$k + 3 + k + 2 =$$

14 I have a square grid and two rectangles.

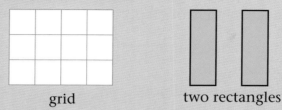

grid   two rectangles

I make a pattern with the grid and the two rectangles:

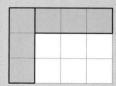   The pattern has *no* lines of symmetry

(a) Copy the grid below:

   Put both rectangles on the grid to make a pattern with *two* lines of symmetry.

You must *shade* the rectangles.

(b) Copy the grid below:

   Put both rectangles on the grid to make a pattern with only one *line* of symmetry.

You must *shade* the rectangles.

(c) Copy the grid below:

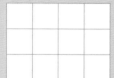   Put both rectangles on the grid to make a pattern with *rotation* symmetry of *order 2*.

You must *shade* the rectangles.

15 Write down the missing number in each box.

(a) $\frac{1}{2}$ of 10 = $\frac{1}{4}$ of ☐

(b) $\frac{3}{4}$ of 100 = $\frac{1}{2}$ of ☐

(c) $\frac{1}{3}$ of 90 = $\frac{2}{3}$ of ☐

194

16 Solve these equations (this means 'find the value of k'):

(a) $6k - 1 = 11$ 　　　　　　　　(b) $2k + 7 = 12$

17 (a) There are four people in Ann's family.
　　　Their shoe sizes are 3, 6, 8 and 11.
　　　What is the *median* shoe size in Ann's family?

　　(b) There are *three* people in Harry's family.
　　　The *range* of their shoe sizes is 5.
　　　Two people in the family wear shoe size 7.
　　　Harry's shoe size is *not 7* and it is *not 12*.
　　　What is Harry's shoe size?

18 On this square grid, *A and B must not move.*

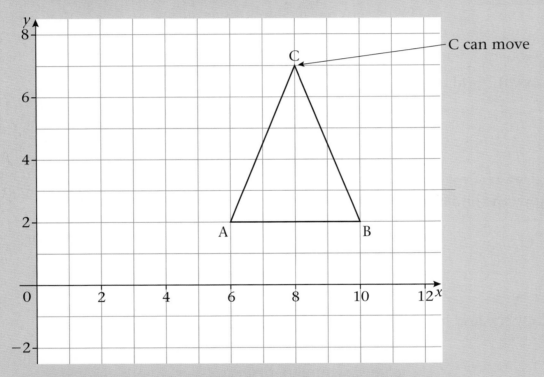

When C is at (8, 7), triangle ABC is *isosceles*.

(a) C moves so that triangle ABC is still *isosceles*.
　　Where could C have moved to?
　　Write the co-ordinates of its new position. (. . . , . . .)

(b) Now C moves so that triangle ABC is isosceles and right-angled.
　　Where could C have moved to?
　　Write the co-ordinates of its new position. (. . . , . . .)

19 A car park shows this sign.

CAR PARKING
80p

Pay using only these coins
10p   20p   50p

NO CHANGE GIVEN

Copy and complete the table below to show all the *different ways* of paying exactly *80p*.

Number of 10p coins	Number of 20p coins	Number of 50p coins
8	0	0

20 *Use compasses* to construct a triangle that has sides *8 cm, 6 cm* and *5 cm*.

Leave in your construction lines.

Start by drawing an 8 cm line:

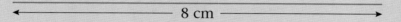

8 cm

21 (a) I pay *£14.20* to travel to work each week.

I work for *45 weeks* each year.

How much do I pay to travel to work each year?

(b) I could buy one season ticket that would let me travel for *all 45 weeks*.

It would cost *£540*.

How much is that per week?

You may use a calculator but remember to show your working out.

(1) Look at this diagram.

It shows distances in miles between some cities.

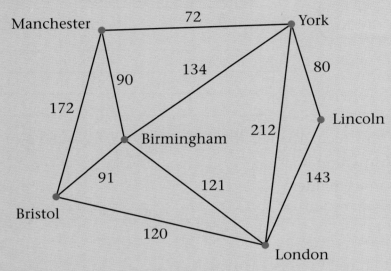

(a) How far is it from *London* to *Lincoln*?

(b) Which 2 cities are *172 miles* apart?

(c) Ivan lives in London.

He wants to visit either *Bristol* or *Birmingham*.

Which of these two cities is *nearer* to *London*?

(d) Sanjay drives from *Birmingham to York*, then he drives *to Manchester*, and then he drives directly *to Birmingham*.

How many miles does he drive altogether?

(2) Look at these shapes.

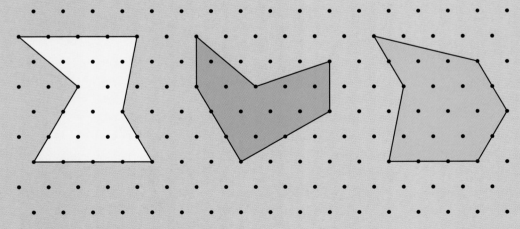

Explain why the shapes are *hexagons*.

3 Look at these three number cards.

| 0 | 8 | 3 |

You can put them together to show different numbers.

For example: | 0 | 8 | 3 | eighty-three

(a) Put the three cards together in a different way by copying and filling in the empty boxes below:

| | 0 | | Write *in words* what number the cards show.

(b) Now put the three cards together in another different way.

| | | 0 | Write *in words* what number the cards show.

(c) Here are three different number cards.

| 1 | 6 | 7 |

Write down the *biggest* number you can show with these three cards.

(d) Write down the *biggest even* number you can show with the three cards in part c).

4 A school records how many pupils are late each day.
The bar charts show the results for one week.

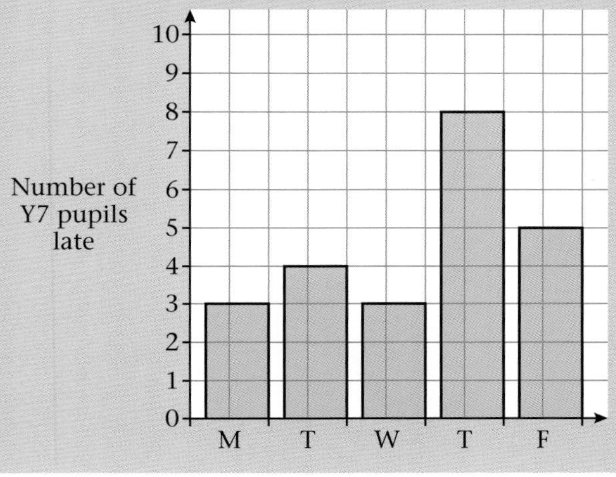

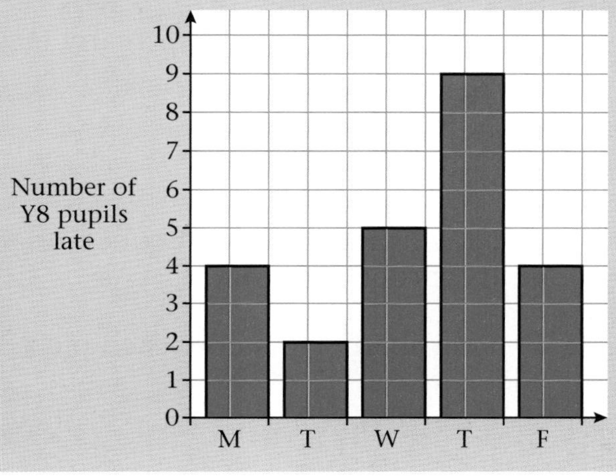

Number of Y7 pupils late

Number of Y8 pupils late

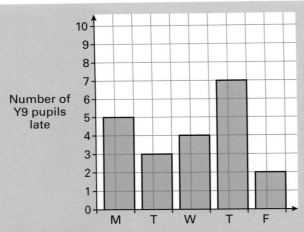

(a) *Altogether*, how many pupils were late on *Friday*?

(b) *Altogether*, how many lates were recorded for *Y8* pupils?

(c) The school bus broke down on one of the days.

Which day do you think that was?

Explain why you chose that day.

5 Millie and Frank each buy a bicycle but they pay in different ways.

| Millie pays £229.99 | Frank pays £9.68 every week for 26 weeks |

Frank pays more than Millie. How much more?

6 (a) I slice a cube in half like this:

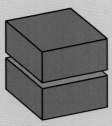

How many faces does each piece have?

(b) Now I slice another cube in half like this:

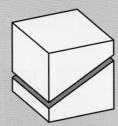

How many faces does each piece have?

(c) Now I slice a different cube in half through its corners like this:

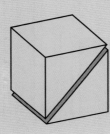

How many faces does each piece have?

7 (a) The thermometer shows Tim's temperature.

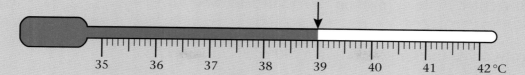

Tim's normal temperature is *37.0°C*.

How many degrees *higher than normal* is Tim's temperature?

(b) On Monday morning, Shula's temperature was *39.1°C*.

By Tuesday morning, Shula's temperature had *fallen* by *1.4°C*.

What was Shula's temperature on Tuesday morning?

(c) You can measure temperature in °C or in °F.

The diagram shows how to change °F to °C.

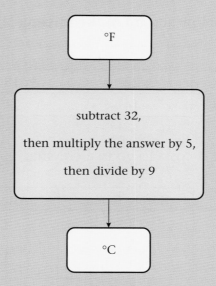

The highest temperature ever recorded in a human was *116.1°F*.

What is this temperature in °C? Show your working.

8 Justin did a survey.

He asked pupils in his school:

'Do you like the colour of the school uniforms?'

The table shows his results.

	Yes	No	Don't know
Year 7	37	15	3
Year 8	21	27	6
Year 9	19	16	7

(a) How many pupils from *Year 8* took part in the survey?

(b) Altogether, more pupils said '*Yes*' than said '*No*'.

How many more?

(c) Justin asked the same question to *80 pupils* in *Year 11*.

25% said '*Yes*'. *50%* said '*No*'. The rest said '*Don't know*'.

Copy and complete the table below to show how many pupils from Year 11 gave each answer.

	Yes	No	Don't know
Year 11			

(d) Christine does a different survey with pupils in Year 9. She wants to know if more boys than girls have pets.

She asks: 'Do you have a pet?'

Copy her results table below and fill in the missing labels.

. . . .	. . . .	. . . .
. . . .	22	18
. . . .	14	21

9 The table shows how much it costs to go to a cinema.

	Before 6 p.m.	After 6 p.m.
Adult	£3.80	£5.50
Child (14 or under)	£2.70	£3.70
Senior Citizen (60 or over)	£2.95	£4.90

Mrs Sims (aged 35), her son (aged 12) and a friend (aged 65) want to go to the cinema.

They are not sure whether to go before 6 p.m. or after 6 p.m.

How much will they save if they go *before* 6 p.m?

10 In this question, use squared paper.

(a) Draw a *rectangle* that has an area of *20 cm²*.

(b) Draw another rectangle that has an area of 20 cm².

This rectangle must have a *different perimeter* from the rectangle in part a).

(c) Draw a *triangle* that has an area of *10 cm²*.

11 I have two bags of cubes.

Each bag contains more than 19 but fewer than 25 cubes.

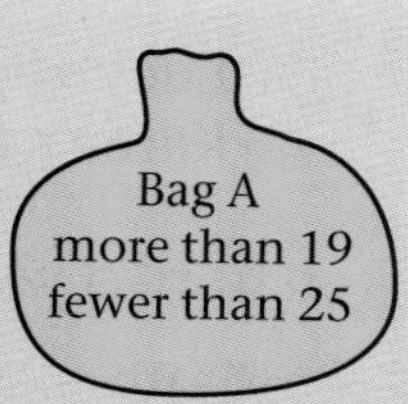

Bag A
more than 19
fewer than 25

(a) I can *share* the cubes in bag A *equally between* 8 people.

How many cubes are in bag A?

(b)

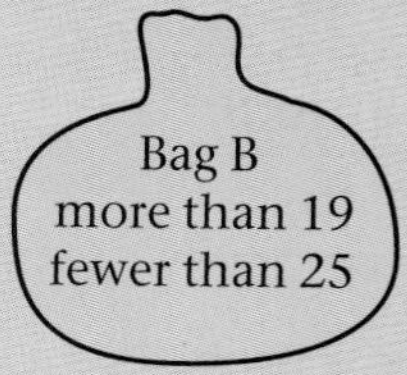

Bag B
more than 19
fewer than 25

I can *share* the cubes in bag B *equally between* 3 people.

How many cubes could be in bag B?

There are *two* answers. Write them both.

12 Each diagram below was drawn on a square grid.

Write what percentage of each diagram is red.

The first one is done for you.

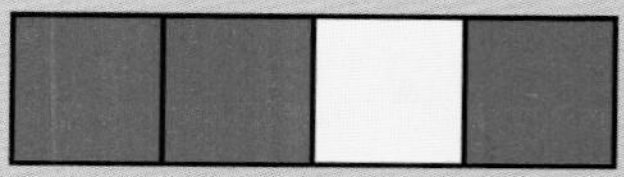

75%

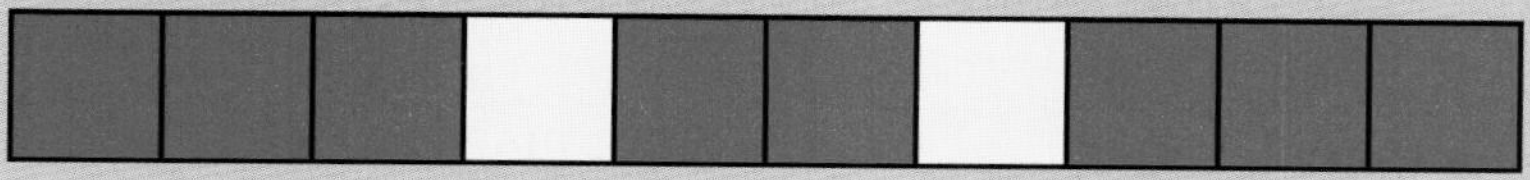

(a) . . . . %

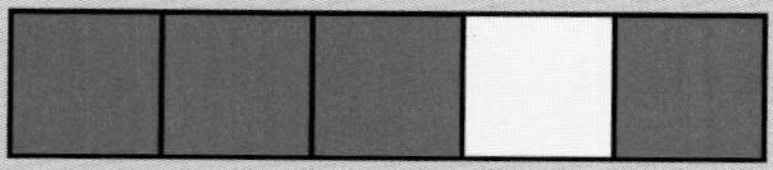

(b) . . . . %

(c) Explain how you know that 25% of the diagram below is red.

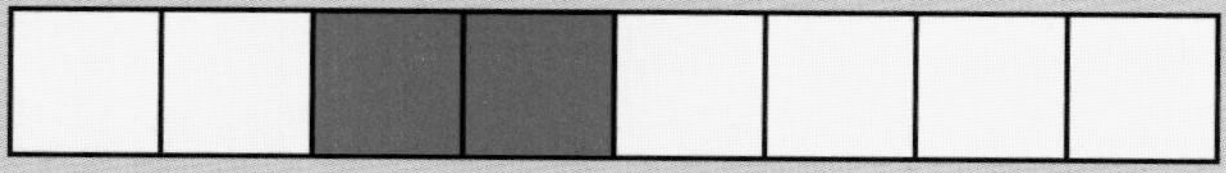

(d) Copy the diagram below and shade $12\frac{1}{2}$%.

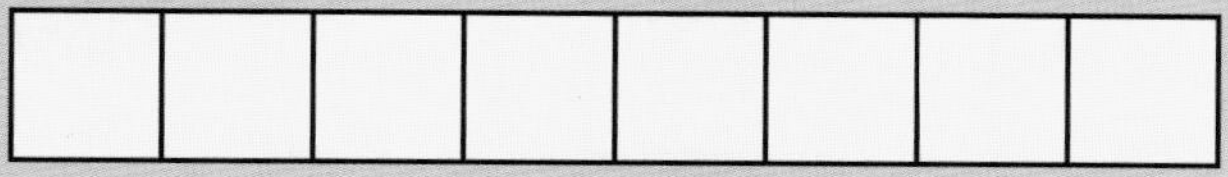

13 It is Lucy's birthday. We do not know how old Lucy is.

Call *Lucy's age*, in years, n.

The expressions below compare Lucy's age to some other peoples' ages.

Use words to compare their ages. The first one is done for you.

Lucy's age	n
Rachel's age	$n + 4$

Rachel is | 4 years older than Lucy |

(a)
Lucy's age	n
Asif's age	$n - 2$

Asif is | |

(b)

Lucy's age	n
Karen's age	$3n$

Karen is ☐

(c) In two years' time Lucy's age will be $n + 2$.

Write *simplified expressions* to show the ages of the other people in two years' time (copy and complete the table below).

	Lucy	Rachel	Asif	Karen
Age now	n	$n + 4$	$n - 2$	$3n$
Age in two year's time	$n + 2$	....	....	....

(d) When $n = 40$, find the value of $2n + 2$.

(e) When $n = 40$, find the value of $2(n + 2)$.

(14) Some pupils plan a survey to find the most common types of tree in a wood.

Plan 1	Plan 2	Plan 3
Write down the type of each tree that you see. *For example*: elm, oak, elm, elm, sycamore, ash	Use these codes to record the type of each tree that you see. Ash A Birch B Elm E Oak O Sycamore S *For example*: E, O, E, E, S, A, ...	Use a tally chart to record the type of each tree that you see. *For example*: Type of tree / Tally Ash Birch Elm Oak Sycamore Other

The pupils will only use *one plan*.

(a) Write down which plan they should *not* use.

Explain why it is not a good plan to use.

(b) Write down the plan that is best.

Explain why it is the best.

15 Look at the diagram.

Triangle ABD is the reflection of triangle ABC in the line AB.

Copy the sentences below to explain how to find angle *x*.

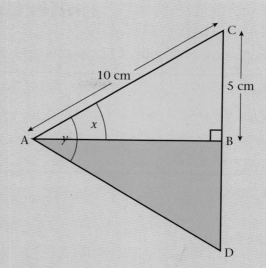

The length of AC is . . 10 . . . . cm.

The length of AD is . . . . cm.

The length of CD is . . . . cm.

ACD is an *equilateral* triangle because . . . .

so angle *y* is . . . . ° because . . . .

so angle *x* is . . . . ° because . . . .

16 (a) Mo has these *4 coins*.

Mo is going to take one of these coins at random.

Each coin is equally likely to be the one she takes.

Show that the *probability* that it will be a *20p* coin is $\frac{1}{2}$.

(b) Ed has four coins that total 73p.

He is going to take one of his coins at random.

What is the probability that it will be a *20p* coin?

You *must* show your working.

17 (a) A glass holds 275 ml.

One day an adult drinks 2.2 litres of water.

How many glasses is that?

Show your working.

(b) An adult weighs 70 kg.

60% of his total mass is water.

What is the mass of this water?

On these pages you will collect like terms and multiply out more brackets.

Remember

$3a + 2b + 4b + 5a$

$= 8a + 6b$

$4(a + 3) = 4a + 12$

$5p + 6q - 2q$

$= 5p + 4q$

$6(2x - 4) = 12x - 24$

M

Collect like terms

1 $7x + 3y + 9x$

2 $8x + 2y + 3y$

3 $4a + 6a + 3b$

4 $5a + 7a + 9$

5 $8a + 3 + 4a$

6 $6x + 3y - 2x$

7 $5x + 10y - 3y$

8 $10a - 7a + 4b$

9 $3a + 12b - 6b$

10 $6x + 3y - 2y$

11 $6b + 4c - 2c + 4b$

12 $9x - 8c + 3d - d$

13 $4x - 2x + 9x + 1$

14 $7x + 7 - 5 - 1$

15 $3 + 8a + 12a - 3a$

Remove the brackets

16 $2(x + 5)$

17 $4(x + 7)$

18 $7(a + 6)$

19 $4(a - 3)$

20 $9(x - 2)$

21 $6(a - 9)$

22 $4(2a + 3)$

23 $2(3a + 5)$

24 $10(5a - 2)$

25 $3(3a - 5)$

26 $6(4b - 2)$

27 $8(4 + 3x)$

28 $8(2 - x)$

29 $4(x + y)$

30 $7(2x + y)$

E

Collect like terms

1 $8a + 4a + 3b + 2a + 9b$

2 $6a + 2b - 3a + 9b - b$

3 $8x - 3x + 7y - 2x - 2y$

4 $4a + 6b + 9b - 2b + 4a$

5 $6x + 8y - 2y - 4x + 2y$

6 $9x + 6y - 3y + 2 - 3x$

7 $6m + 4m - 2m + 3n - 2m$

8 $6a + 3a + 6b - 3b + 4b$

9 $12a - 5a + 2a + 2 - 4a$

10 $14x + 6y + 6 - 3x + 9y + 8x$

Remove the brackets

11 $7(3a + 2)$

12 $8(2x + 1)$

13 $10(3x - 4)$

14 $6(3x - 8)$

15 $12(4 + 6x)$

16 $5(9 - 7x)$

Find the perimeters of the following shapes.

17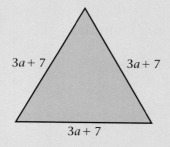

3a + 7   3a + 7

3a + 7

19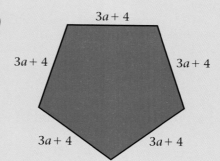

3a + 4

3a + 4   3a + 4

3a + 4   3a + 4

18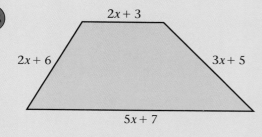

2x + 3

2x + 6   3x + 5

5x + 7

20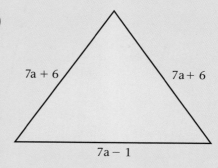

7a + 6   7a + 6

7a − 1

Find the areas of the following shapes. Remove the brackets in your answers.

21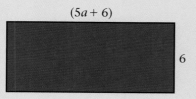

(5a + 6)

6

23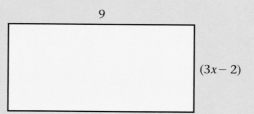

9

(3x − 2)

22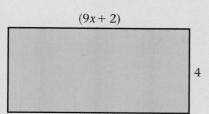

(9x + 2)

4

24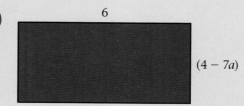

6

(4 − 7a)

Find both the area and the perimeter of each of the following shapes.

25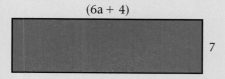

(6a + 4)

7

26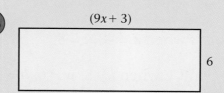

(9x + 3)

6

On this page you will put numbers in place of letters in expressions and formulas.

M

In Questions **1** to **16** find the value of each expression when $a = 5$, $b = 2$ and $c = 3$.

1	$a + b$	**5**	$4(a + b)$	**9**	$b(a + c)$	**13**	$b^2 + c^2$
2	$2a + c$	**6**	$3(a - c)$	**10**	$a(b + c)$	**14**	abc
3	$2a - b$	**7**	$5a - 6c$	**11**	$(2a)^2$	**15**	$b(2a - c)$
4	$a + b + c$	**8**	$a^2 + b$	**12**	$\frac{a + c}{2}$	**16**	$\frac{3c + a}{b}$

E

1

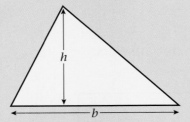

Area of triangle = (base × height) then ÷ 2

we say $A = \dfrac{bh}{2}$

Find A when:

(a) $b = 4$ and $h = 3$ (c) $b = 14$ and $h = 8$

(b) $b = 12$ and $h = 4$ (d) $b = 10$ and $h = 16$

2 A formula in Science tells us that $\boxed{V = IR}$. Find V when:

(a) $I = 8$ and $R = 9$ (c) $I = 42$ and $R = 85$

(b) $I = 4$ and $R = 20$ (d) $I = 0.5$ and $R = 160$

3 Another formula in Science tells us that $\boxed{v = u + at}$. Find v when:

(a) $u = 10$, $a = 10$ and $t = 8$ (c) $u = 30$, $a = 50$ and $t = 60$

(b) $u = 20$, $a = 5$ and $t = 9$ (d) $u = 37$, $a = 5$ and $t = 18$

4 $A = lw$. Find A when $l = 9$, $w = 16$

5 $s = \dfrac{d}{t}$. Find s when $d = 48$, $t = 8$

6 $V = lwh$. Find V when $l = 5$, $w = 6$, $h = 7$

7 $D = \dfrac{M}{V}$. Find D when $M = 144$, $V = 8$

On these pages you will draw straight line graphs.

Look at the section 'Straight Lines 1' earlier in the book if you need a reminder.

For each Question you will need to draw axes like these:

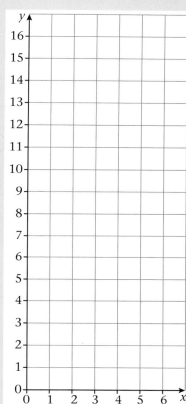

1 $y = x + 7$

Complete the co-ordinates:

(0, 7) (1, 8) (2, ☐) (3, ☐) (4, ☐)

Plot these points and draw the graph.

2 $y = 3x + 4$

Complete the co-ordinates:

(0, 4) (1, 7) (2, ☐) (3, ☐) (4, ☐)

Plot these points and draw the graph.

3 $y = 6 - x$

Complete the co-ordinates:

(0, 6) (1, ☐) (2, ☐) (3, ☐) (4, ☐)

Plot these points and draw the graph.

4 $y = 2x - 4$

Complete the co-ordinates:

(2, 0)(3, ☐)(4, ☐)(5, ☐)(6, ☐)

Draw the graph.

5 $y = 5x + 1$

Complete the co-ordinates:

(0,1) (1, ☐) (2, ☐) (3, ☐)

Draw the graph.

6 $y = 4x - 2$

Complete the co-ordinates:

(1, 2) (2, ☐) (3, ☐) (4, ☐)

Draw the graph.

Note

Check all your graphs with a computer or graphical calculator if your teacher wants you to.

Sometimes we use *negative numbers* for *values of x*.

To draw the line $y = 2x - 1$, we begin by working out the y values for different values of x. In this case we take x from -2 to $+3$.

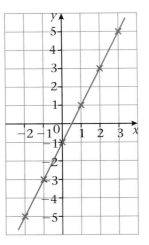

when $x = -2$, $y = 2 \times (-2) - 1 = -5$

$x = -1$, $y = 2 \times (-1) - 1 = -3$

$x = 0$, $y = 2 \times (0) - 1 = -1$

$x = 1$, $y = 2 \times (1) - 1 = 1$

$x = 2$, $y = 2 \times (2) - 1 = 3$

$x = 3$, $y = 2 \times (3) - 1 = 5$

The points $(-2, -5)$, $(-1, -3)$ ... $(3, 5)$ are plotted and a line is drawn through them.

E

1 The equation of a line is $y = 2x + 2$.

Copy and complete this list of co-ordinates.

$x = -2$, $y = 2x + 2 = 2 \times (-2) + 2 = -2$ $(-2, -2)$

$x = -1$, $y = 2 \times (-1) + 2 = \boxed{}$ $(-1, \boxed{})$

$x = 0$, $y = 2 \times (0) + 2 = \boxed{}$ $(0, \boxed{})$

$x = 1$, $y = 2 \times (1) + 2 = \boxed{}$ $(1, \boxed{})$

$x = 2$, $y = 2 \times (2) + 2 = \boxed{}$ $(2, \boxed{})$

$x = 3$, $y = \ldots\ldots\ldots = \boxed{}$ $(3, \boxed{})$

$x = 4$, $y = \ldots\ldots\ldots = \boxed{}$ $(4, \boxed{})$

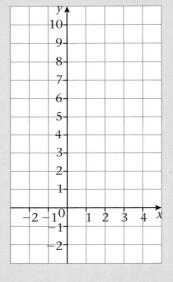

Draw these axes on squared paper.

Plot the 7 points above.

Join up the points to make a straight line.

The equation of this line is $y = 2x + 2$.

In Questions **2** to **5** below, take x-values from -3 to 3 and use the equation to find the y-values.

For each Question, draw an x-axis from -3 to 3 and a y-axis so that all the points can be plotted. For each Question, plot all the points and join them up to make a straight line.

2 $y = x + 5$ **3** $y = 2x - 3$ **4** $y = 3x + 2$ **5** $y = 2x + 3$

Look at the miniature chess board below. It is only a 4 × 4 square instead of 8 × 8. Your problem is to place four objects on the board so that nowhere are there two objects on the same row (↔), column (↕) or diagonal (↗) (↘).

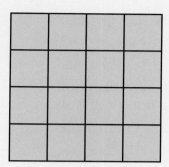

In the example below we have gone wrong because **1** and **4** are on the same diagonal, and **2** and **3** are on the other diagonal.

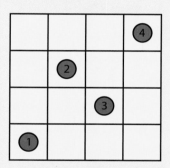

1 Find a correct answer for the 4 × 4 square.

2 Find an answer for a 5 × 5 square, using 5 objects.

3 Now you have to find an answer for a 6 × 6 square, using six objects. (Try to find a system by looking at what you have done in Questions **1** and **2**. Do not just guess!)

4 Use your system to find an answer for a 7 × 7 square, using seven objects.

5 Finally, if you have been successful with the previous squares, try to find an answer for a full 8 × 8 square, using eight objects. (It is called the chess board problem because one of the objects could be a 'Queen' which can move any number of squares in any direction.)

Problem Solving 2

On these pages you will use diagrams to find patterns and formulas to solve problems.

Ⓜ

Pond Borders

A pond has a border of paving slabs.

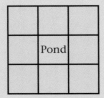

We will call this pond 1.
It has a border of 8 slabs.

A larger pond is made as below.

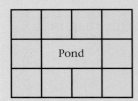

We will call this pond 2.
It has a border of 10 slabs.

A larger pond 3 is shown below

| Pond |

① How many slabs are in the border of pond 3?

② Draw pond 4.

③ How many slabs are in the border of pond 4?

④ How many slabs are needed for the border of pond 5?

⑤ How many slabs are needed for the border of pond 6?

⑥ Copy and complete the table below:

Pond Number n	Number of slabs s
1	
2	
3	
4	
5	
6	

7 Is there a pattern for the number of slabs?
They should increase by the same number each time.

8 There will be a two-stage rule which connects the 'number of slabs' with the 'pond number' as below. Copy and fill in the empty boxes.

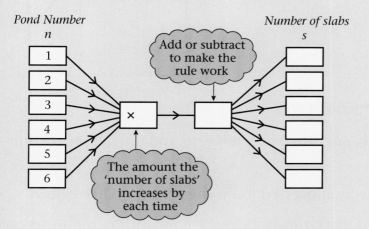

9 Can you write your rule as a formula?

(*Example* If rule is $n \rightarrow \times 5 \rightarrow + 3 \rightarrow s$ then s = 5n + 3.)

10 It is *VERY IMPORTANT* to *CHECK* your rule.

Use n = 7 in your formula to find s.

Now *draw* pond 7.

Count the number of slabs. Did you get the same answer using the formula?

Hopefully you did!

11 Use your formula to find the number of slabs needed for pond 100.

This is *much easier* than drawing pond 100!

12 Use your formula to find the number of slabs needed for pond 500.

13 Which pond number needed 306 slabs?

14 Which pond number needed 156 slabs?

15 Ask your teacher to explain the formula to you by using the diagrams below:

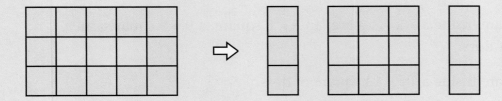

How many dots?

The diagram shows a 5 × 5 square of dots.

There are 16 dots *on the perimeter*.

There are 9 dots *inside the square*.

1 Draw a 3 × 3, a 4 × 4 and a 6 × 6 square of dots.

For each diagram, count the number of dots *on the perimeter* and the number of dots *inside the square*.

2 Make a table of your results for the 'number of dots on the perimeter' like below:

Square s	Dots on Perimeter d
3	
4	
5	
6	

3 Find a pattern and a formula.

4 *Check* your formula works by drawing a 7 × 7 square of dots.

5 For a 100 × 100 square of dots, how many dots are on the perimeter?

6 Make a table of your results for the 'number of dots inside each square' like below:

Square s	Dots inside square D
3	
4	
5	
6	

7 Can you find a pattern?

8 How many dots are inside a 7 × 7 square, an 8 × 8 square, a 9 × 9 square and a 10 × 10 square of dots?

9 How many dots are inside a 14 × 14 square of dots?

10 Write down anything else about doing this problem that you feel is useful.

On this page you will find the value of one item to help you find the value of several items.

Reminder

If 5 magazines cost £15, how much will 8 magazines cost?

Find the cost of one magazine.

1 magazine costs £15 ÷ 5 = £3

so 8 magazines cost £3 × 8 = £24

M

1. 6 bars of chocolate cost £1.80. How much will 10 bars cost?

2. 4 kg of apples cost 64p. How much will 7 kg cost?

3. A car travels 150 miles in 3 hrs. How far will it go in 4 hrs at the same speed?

4. A space ship travels 5 times around the world in 400 minutes. How long will it take to go around the world 9 times?

5. 8 cm² of skin can be tattooed in 1 hr and 20 minutes. How long will it take to tattoo 15 cm²?

6. 3 CDs play for a total of $1\frac{1}{2}$ hrs. How long will 5 CDs play for?

7. A farmer needs 70 litres of milk to make 5 kg of cheese. How much will he need to make 8 kg of cheese?

8. 7 bottles of water were needed to fill 63 plastic cups. How many bottles would be needed to fill 180 cups?

E

1. A 56 gallon tank takes 7 minutes to fill. How long did it take to put in 24 gallons?

2. A butcher needs 800 g of pork to make 16 sausages. How much pork will he need to make 40 sausages?

3. 150 000 tonnes of concrete are needed to lay 6 miles of motorway. How much would be needed for 17 miles?

4. A supermarket chain orders 42 000 bottles of wine to supply 60 of its stores. How many bottles would be needed for 75 stores?

5. 171 000 cars passed a breakdown on the M25 in 90 minutes. How many passed in the first 4 minutes?

Reminder

A *diagonal* in a quadrilateral is a line which joins one vertex (corner) to the opposite vertex (corner).

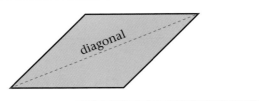

M

1 (a) Draw a *square*.

(b) Draw the diagonals.

(c) Measure how long the diagonals are.

(d) Use a protractor to measure the angles between the two diagonals.

(e) Copy and complete below:
'A square has f _ _ _ _ _ e _ _ _ _ _ _ sides. All its angles are _ _ _ _ degrees. The angles between the diagonals are _ _ _ degrees. It has _ _ _ _ lines of symmetry'.

2 (a) Draw a *rectangle*.

(b) Draw the diagonals.

(c) Measure how long the diagonals are.

(d) Copy and complete below:
'A rectangle has f _ _ _ _ _ sides. All its angles are_ _ _ _ _ _ degrees. The diagonals are e _ _ _ _ _ _ _ _ in length. It has _ _ _ _ _ lines of symmetry'.

3 (a) Draw a *rhombus*.

(b) Draw the diagonals.

(c) Use a protractor to measure the angles between the two diagonals.

(d) Copy and complete below:
'A rhombus has f_ _ _ _ _ e _ _ _ _ _ sides. It has _ _ _ _ _ _ lines of symmetry. The angles between the diagonals are _ _ _ _ _ _ _ degrees'.

4 (a) Draw a *parallelogram*.

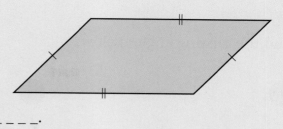

(b) Use a protractor to measure the four angles inside the parallelogram.

(c) Copy and complete below:
'A parallelogram has f_ _ _ _ _ _ sides.
The opposite sides are e_ _ _ _ _ and p_ _ _ _ _ _.
The opposite angles are e_ _ _ _ _ _ _ _.'

5 (a) Draw a *kite*.

(b) Draw the diagonals.

(c) Use a protractor to measure the angles between the two diagonals.

(d) Copy and complete below:
'A kite has f_ _ _ _ _ _ sides. It has _ _ _ _ _ _ line of symmetry.
Its diagonals cross at _ _ _ _ _ _ _ degrees'.

6 (a) Draw an isosceles *trapezium*.

(b) Copy and complete below:
'A trapezium has f _ _ _ _ _ sides. It has just one pair of sides which are p _ _ _ _ _ _ _ _ _ _ _ _ _ _ _ _'.

Reminder

An *isosceles* triangle has two equal sides only and two equal angles only.

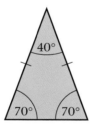
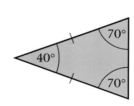

Look at the two equal sides and notice where the two equal angles are.

Example

Find angle *a* in the triangle shown.

The triangle is isosceles, so PR̂Q = *a*.

The sum of the angles in a triangle is 180°.

$$a + a + 44 = 180$$

$$a = 68°$$

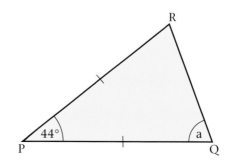

Find the missing angles below:

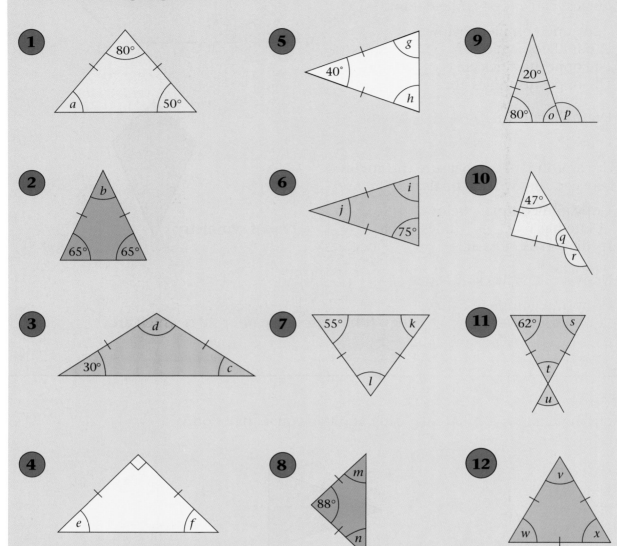

13 In each of the three triangles below, the length of one side can be found.
Write down the side which can be found and its length.

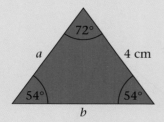

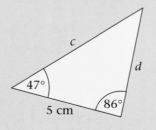

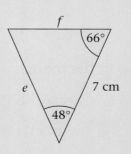

On these pages you will state a hypothesis, collect data, process data and interpret the data.

Ⓜ

Task 1

Can taller people hold their breath longer than shorter people?

1. What do you think? Write down what you think. This is your 'hypothesis'. Related Questions; What is 'tall'? Above what height would you choose?

2. How many people will you ask to hold their breath? Who will you ask? (Your teacher may say 'only pupils in your class'.)

3. How many times will you ask each person to hold their breath so that you get more reliable results?

4. Design a data collection sheet. One example is given below:

Name	Height (cm)	1st go (secs)	2nd go (secs)	3rd go (secs)	Longest time (secs)

Now collect your data (*check* with your teacher that you have got enough data when you have finished).

5. Put your data into groups by making tables like this below:

Time (secs)	Frequency
10–19	1
20–29	2
30–39	4
40–49	7

Make one table for shorter people and one table for taller people.

Note

Use a computer if possible to make these.

6 Draw a diagram to show your data.
Draw one diagram for the shorter people
and one diagram for the taller people.

A possible diagram is shown:

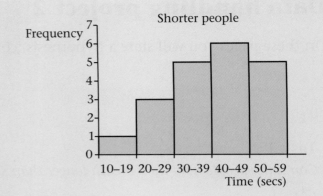

7 Would a pie chart show the data in a better way? Can you draw a pie chart?
(Use a computer if possible.)

8 Copy and complete the table below (you may use a calculator).
Check with your teacher.

	Median	Mean	Range
Shorter people			
Taller people			

9 *Conclusion*

(a) Copy and complete the following sentences:
'The median for shorter people is (greater/smaller) than the median for taller
people. The mean for shorter people is (greater/smaller) than the mean for
taller people. The range for shorter people is (greater/smaller) than the range
for taller people (i.e. the 'holding breath' times for shorter people is (more/less)
spread out).'

(b) Was your hypothesis correct?

(c) Write down anything else about doing this problem that you feel is useful.

YOUR TEACHER WILL ASK YOU TO WORK THROUGH THE PROJECT BELOW *OR* TO PICK YOUR OWN TOPIC.

Task 2 Hypothesis

The most likely time for a goal to be scored during football matches in the English Premiership league is during the last 5 minutes of the first half or the second half.

1   What do you think?

You must collect data to show if this hypothesis is true or not. (Each half of a football match is 45 minutes long.)

2   What data do you need to collect? How much do you need?

3   How are you going to collect the data? From newspapers? From the Internet? From somewhere else?

Agree with your teacher as to where you are going to get the data. Now collect your data.

4   Put your data into groups by making tables like below:

First Half	
Time (minutes)	Goals scored
1–5	
11–15	
16–20	
21–25	
26–30	
31–35	
36–40	
41–45	

Make another table for the Second Half.

Note
Use a computer if possible to make these.

5   Draw a chart to show your data for the First Half. Draw a chart to show your data for the Second Half.

6   (a)   In which group are most goals scored? This is called the modal group (the mode).
      (b)   Is the hypothesis for this task true or not?
          Write down all your reasons.
      (c)   Write down anything else about doing this problem that you feel is useful.

On these pages you will learn how to put data into a stem and leaf diagram and how to interpret a stem and leaf diagram.

Data can be displayed in groups in a stem and leaf diagram.
Here are the marks of 20 girls in a science test.

47	53	71	55	28	40	45	62	57	64
33	48	59	61	73	37	75	26	68	39

We will put the marks into groups 20–29, 30–39.:... 70–79.

We will choose the tens digit as the 'stem' and the units as the 'leaf'.

The first four marks are shown [47, 53, 71, 55]

Stem (tens)	Leaf (units)
2	
3	
4	7
5	3 5
6	
7	1

The complete diagram is below . . . . and then with the leaves in numerical order:

Stem	Leaf
2	8 6
3	3 7 9
4	7 0 5 8
5	3 5 7 9
6	2 4 1 8
7	1 3 5

Stem	Leaf
2	6 8
3	3 7 9
4	0 5 7 8
5	3 5 7 9
6	1 2 4 8
7	1 3 5

We write a key next to the stem and leaf diagram to explain what the stem digit means and what the leaf digit means.

In this example   Key 4|7 = 47

The diagram shows the shape of the distribution. It is also easy to find the mode, the median and the range.

Ⓜ

① Here is the stem and leaf diagram showing the weights, in pounds, of animals in a pet shop.

(a) Write down the range of the masses.
(b) How many animals were in the shop?
(c) What is the median weight?

Stem		Leaf
1		2 5 8
2		1 3
3		2 7 8 8
4		5 6

1|2 means 12

② The stem and leaf diagram shows the number of points scored by the England rugby team.

(a) How many games were played?
(b) Find the range of the points scored.

Stem		Leaf
1		2 2 5 7 8
2		1 2 2 4 4 4 7 8
3		1 2 3 3 4 5
4		4 4 6 8 8
5		1

Key 1|2 = 12 points

③ Here are two stem and leaf diagrams showing the marks of children in two tests, Maths and Science.

Maths:

Stem		Leaf
2		8
3		3 4 5 8
4		2 4 7 7 9
5		1

Key 2|8 = 28

Science:

Stem		Leaf
2		1 2 5
3		6 7
4		5 6
5		5 7
6		3 8

(a) What was the median mark for each test?

(b) What was the range for each test?

(c) In which test were the marks spread out more widely?

1 Here are the marks of 13 pupils in a spelling test:

| 41 | 32 | 50 | 44 | 62 | 68 | 71 | 54 | 47 | 35 | 68 | 55 | 56 |

Stem	Leaf
3	2
4	1
5	0
6	
7	

Key 3|2 = 32

(a) Using the key shown, draw a stem and leaf diagram. The first three entries are shown.

(b) What was the median mark?

2 The masses of 20 apples from a tree were recorded to the nearest gram.

| 123 | 134 | 121 | 126 | 127 | 135 | 136 | 138 | 140 | 132 |
| 124 | 143 | 139 | 120 | 137 | 133 | 136 | 122 | 141 | 134 |

Stem	Leaf
12	
13	
14	

Key 13|7 = 137

(a) Using the key shown, draw a stem and leaf diagram.

(b) Find the median mass.

3 Draw a stem and leaf diagram for the following data:

2.4	3.1	5.2	4.7	1.4	6.2	4.5	3.3
4.0	6.3	3.7	6.7	4.6	4.9	5.1	5.5
1.8	3.8	4.5	2.4	5.8	3.3	4.6	2.8

Stem	Leaf
1	
2	
3	
4	
5	
6	

Key 3|7 = 3.7

(a) What is the median?

(b) Write down the range.

On these pages you will explore objects by using cubes and draw different views of each shape.

Below are two pictures of the same object.

(a)   On squared paper.

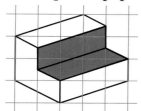

(b)   On isometric dot paper.

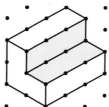

Isometric paper can be used either as dots (as above) or as a grid of equilateral triangles. Either way, the paper must be the right way round (as shown here).

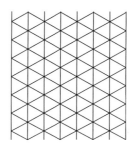

N.B. Most of the questions in this section are easier, and more fun to do, when you have an ample supply of 'unifix' or 'multilink' cubes.

Ⓜ

① On isometric paper make a copy of each object below. Underneath each drawing state the number of 'multilink' cubes needed to make the object. (Make sure you have the isometric paper the right way round!)

(a) 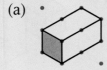   (b) 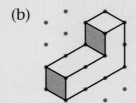   (c)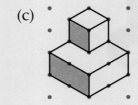

② Make the object shown using cubes.
Now draw the object *from a different view*.

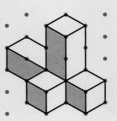

224

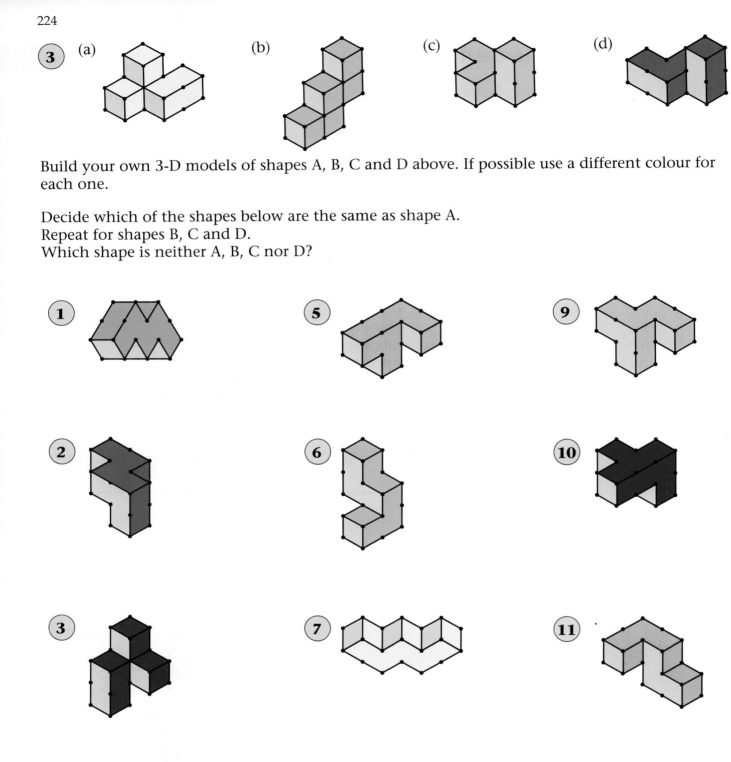

Build your own 3-D models of shapes A, B, C and D above. If possible use a different colour for each one.

Decide which of the shapes below are the same as shape A.
Repeat for shapes B, C and D.
Which shape is neither A, B, C nor D?

E

Three views of a shape
Here is a 3-D object made
from centimetre cubes.

We can draw 3 views of
the object on squared paper.

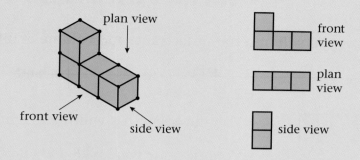

In Questions ① to ⑥ draw the plan view, the front view and the side view of the object

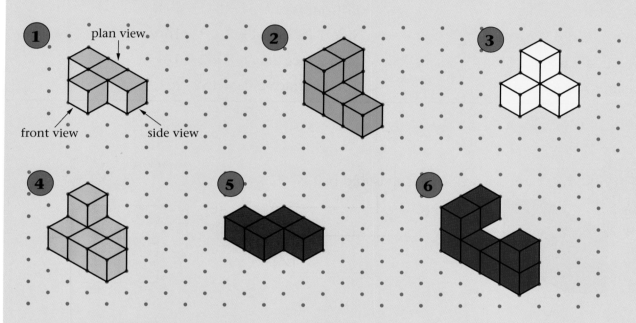

1 plan view
front view   side view

2

3

4

5

6

In Questions ⑦ to ⑩ you are given three views of a shape. Use the information to make
the shape using 'unifix' or 'multilink' cubes.

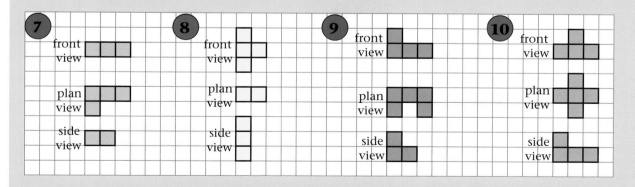

7 front view, plan view, side view

8 front view, plan view, side view

9 front view, plan view, side view

10 front view, plan view, side view

On these pages you will find the surface area and volume of different cuboids.

Example

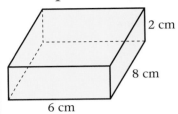

Volume = length × width × height

Volume = 8 × 6 × 2 = 48 × 2 = 96 cm³

There are 6 faces.

Front face area = 6 × 2 = 12

Back face area = 6 × 2 = 12

Top face area = 8 × 6 = 48

Bottom face area = 8 × 6 = 48

Side 1 face area = 8 × 2 = 16

Side 2 face area = 8 × 2 = 16

Total surface area = 152 cm²

Ⓜ

① Find the total surface area of each cuboid below:

(a)

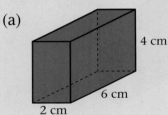

4 cm
6 cm
2 cm

(c)

2 cm
5 cm
10 cm

(e)

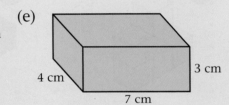

3 cm
4 cm
7 cm

(b)

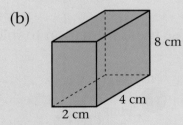

8 cm
4 cm
2 cm

(d)

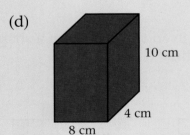

10 cm
4 cm
8 cm

(f)

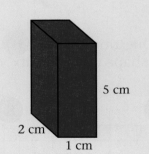

5 cm
2 cm
1 cm

② Find the volumes of the cuboids in the table below:

Object	Length	Width	Height
bar of soap	10 cm	6 cm	3 cm
box of cornflakes	25 cm	20 cm	6 cm
cd	14 cm	12 cm	1 cm
loud-speaker	20 cm	20 cm	15 cm
camping fridge	40 cm	30 cm	60 cm

E

1

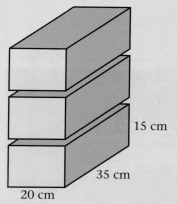

15 cm

35 cm

20 cm

Three shoe boxes measuring

20 cm × 35 cm × 15 cm are stacked on top of each other.

(a) What is the total surface area of the front of the three boxes (shaded on the diagram)?

(b) What is the total volume of the 3 boxes?

2 A bricklayer lays fifty bricks side by side.

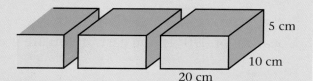

5 cm

10 cm

20 cm

Each brick measures 20 cm × 10 cm × 5 cm.

(a) What is the total surface area of the front of all fifty bricks (shaded blue on the diagram)?

(b) What is the total volume of the fifty bricks?

3

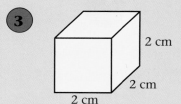

2 cm

2 cm

2 cm

Fifty metal cubes (like the one shown) are melted down. What is the total volume of metal that has been melted down?

4

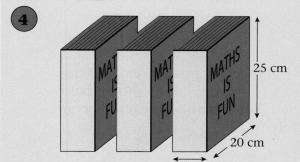

25 cm

20 cm

2 cm

Twenty Maths books can just fit side by side on a shelf.

(a) What is the total surface area of the faces of the twenty books that you can see (blue shaded faces on the diagram)?

(b) What is the total volume of the twenty books?

5 An oil tank measuring 2 m × 0.5 m × 1.2 m is full of oil.

(a) How many cubic metres (m³) of oil does the tank hold?

(b) What is the surface area of the bottom of the tank?

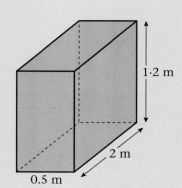

1·2 m

2 m

0.5 m

Bearings

On these pages you will use bearings to give directions and you will use bearings to draw diagrams.

Bearings are used by navigators on ships and aircraft and by people travelling in open country.

> Bearings are measured from north in a *clockwise* direction. A bearing is always given as a three-figure number.

A bearing of 090° is due east. If you are going south-west, you are on a bearing 225°.

James is walking on a bearing of 035°

Mary is walking on a bearing of 146°

Richard is walking on a bearing of 310°

M

1 Ten children on a treasure hunt start in the middle of a field and begin walking in the directions shown on the right. On what bearing is each child walking?

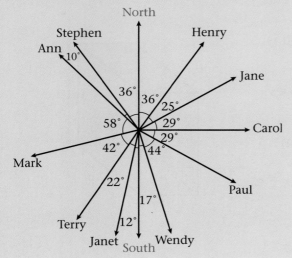

2 Ten pigeons are released and they fly in the directions shown below. On what bearing is each pigeon flying?

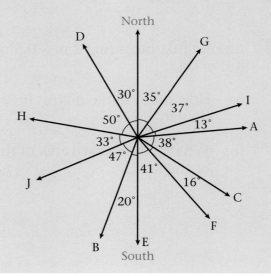

E

1 Use a protractor to measure the bearing on which each person is moving.

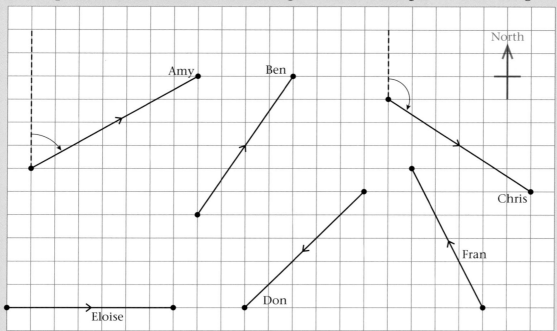

2 Use a protractor to measure the bearing of these journeys.

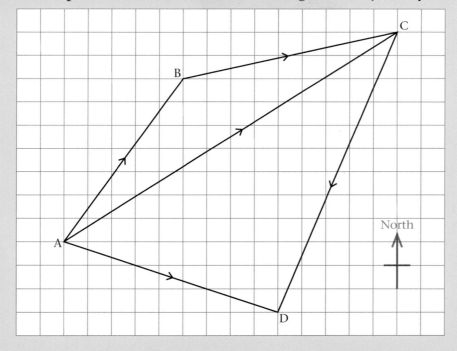

3 Draw lines on the following bearings.

(a) 040°   (b) 075°   (c) 120°   (d) 200°   (e) 300°

4

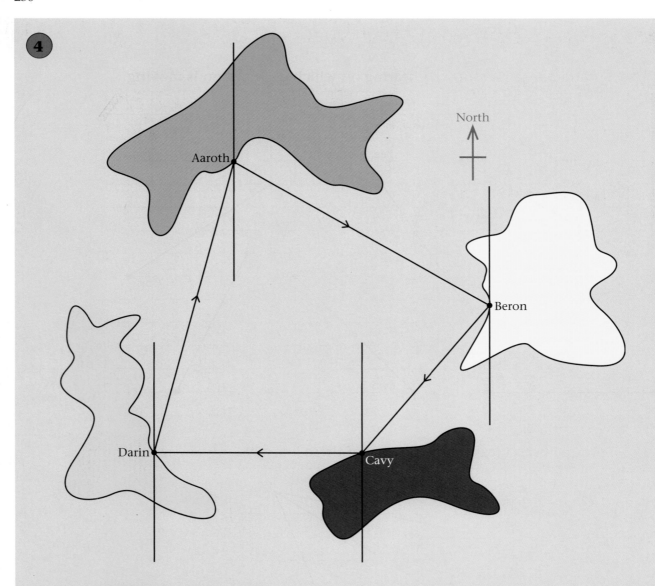

A yacht sails between 4 islands.

It leaves Aaroth and sails directly to Beron then Cavy then Darin then back to Aaroth.

Use a protractor to measure the bearing of the journey from:

(a)   Aaroth to Beron
(b)   Beron to Cavy
(c)   Cavy to Darin
(d)   Darin to Aaroth.
(e)   If the yacht needed to sail directly from Aaroth *back* to Darin, what bearing would it have to take?

Your task is to design square tile patterns of different sizes.

The patterns are all to be made from smaller tiles all of which are themselves square.

(a)   Here is a design for a 4 × 4 square:

   This design consists of four tiles each 2 × 2.
   The pattern is *not* very interesting.

(b)   Now we have a rule that the design must contain at least one 1 × 1 square.

   This design with seven tiles is more interesting.

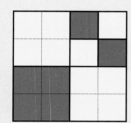

①   Use a 5 × 5 square. Design a pattern which divides the
    5 × 5 square into *exactly* eight smaller squares.
    This diagram shows one way you could start.

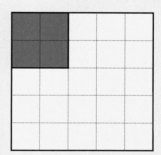

②   Use a 6 × 6 square. *You must include at least one
    1 × 1 square.* Design a pattern which divides the
    6 × 6 square into *exactly* nine smaller squares.
    (Colour in the final design to make it look interesting.)

③   With *no special rules*, design a pattern which divides the
    7 × 7 square into *exactly* nine smaller squares.

④   Design a pattern which divides a 8 × 8 square into *exactly*
    ten smaller squares *but you must not use a 4 × 4 square.*

⑤   Design a pattern which divides a 9 × 9 square into *exactly*
    ten smaller squares *but you can only use one 3 × 3 square.*

⑥   Design a pattern which divides a 10 × 10 square into *exactly*
    eleven smaller squares *but you must include a 3 × 3 square.*